COMPLETE AND FREE

'Mr Williams has sur
depend on his own ta
pleasure—pleasure in th
and driving in the open ...ed, free
of convention . . . a journ... the spirit.'—*The Times*

'A rattling good narrative, high-spirited, taut with sense of adventure, and conveying—possibly best of all—the happiness of two people together.'—*Tatler*

'What he fought for was to be complete and free and this is what, at the heart of it, his book is about . . . Brisk, intelligent and entertaining . . . Eric Williams need nurse no further qualms about his future as a writer.'—*The Sunday Times*

To Jonny,
with all my love for a very happy Christmas (of reading)!
from Julie.

Also by Eric Williams

THE WOODEN HORSE

THE TUNNEL

THE ESCAPERS

COMPLETE AND FREE

ERIC WILLIAMS

UNABRIDGED

PAN BOOKS LTD : LONDON

First published 1957 by Eyre & Spottiswoode (Publishers) Ltd.
This edition published 1959 by Pan Books Ltd.,
8 Headfort Place, London, S.W.1

And to live out of doors with the woman a man loves is of all lives the most complete and free.

ROBERT LOUIS STEVENSON.

Printed in Great Britain by
Wyman & Sons Ltd., London, Fakenham and Reading
and bound by a Flexiback Thermoplastic Binder manufactured by
The Book Machinery Co., Ltd., 124 Westbridge Road, London, S.W.11

CHAPTER ONE

THE OLD open car sat low on her springs under the weight of luggage hidden by the canvas tonneau cover. In our oilskins we pretended to ignore the rain most of which, carried by the wind, passed harmlessly above our heads. The water flung from the wheels sprayed out on each side in streams of silver and the tyres sang on the wet tarmac of the road. Once clear of London we drove fast through Rochester, Chatham and Sittingbourne. Beyond Canterbury, as the light faded from the drenched countryside, we passed a small inn. Through the open door I could see men in the bar and a woman in a red dress drawing a curtain across a window.

"We could stay at a pub," I said.

"Why not camp?" Sibyl was leaning well forward, huddled under the windscreen to get what protection she could from the driving rain.

"There won't be any sun to dry us out in the morning."

"Come on, we've camped in worse than this."

We drove slowly for some miles, peering round the windscreen, the rain beating in our faces. Although the road ahead was brilliantly lit by the headlamps, the hedges on either side were in darkness. I stopped several times to inspect likely places before finally pulling off the road through an open gateway on to the edge of a field of wheat. There was just room to park the car in the lee of a bulging stack of last year's hay where, shielded from the wind, we could pitch the tent in the light of the headlamps. The ground felt soft, and I wondered if we would be able to get on to the road again in the morning. I took off the canvas cover and cursed as the pool of water which had collected on top cascaded down inside my oilskins. Delving into the back of the car I found the torch, and by its light saw Sibyl's smiling face streaming with water, her hair plastered across it in dark streaks. She was enjoying herself.

Soon the small green ridge-tent with its inner envelope of mosquito-netting stood snugly between the haystack and the car. It sagged a little in the middle, but I knew that the ropes would tighten in the night. I spread the dry groundsheet inside the tent and fetched the bedding from the car. By the time I had put up the hood and fastened the tonneau cover across the seats Sibyl had lit the petrol stove to make cocoa. We drank it sweet and hot, listening to the rain beating on the canvas a few inches above our heads.

I awoke before daylight. The rain had stopped and the morning was soft and warm with a thin white mist hanging close to the surface of the ground. Smelling the damp hay and feeling the air cool on my face, I remembered many mornings on the saltings or on the bank of a river when the ice was floating down and it was still and dark over the quiet villages and the duck about to flight. This was the best time of the day, and it had been worth camping, even in the rain.

When the small alarm clock woke me for the second time the sun was shining greenly through the tent and I could see Sibyl curled in her sleeping-bag, her soft hair spread loosely on the rolled shirt she had used as a pillow. The hair by the side of her brown face was bleached fair by the sun and there was a half-smile on her lips.

I shook her by the shoulder. "Wake up—we've got to be alongside by eight-thirty. I'll get the stove going."

While she made the coffee I put up the collapsible table and stools, and then sat drinking from the yellow pottery mug and watched the eggs and bacon sizzle and spit in the frying pan. The smell of the cooking bacon was almost an ache.

The tent was still wet but there was no time to dry it in the sun, and I rolled it stiffly into a tight bundle and forced it into its sack. Then I repacked for the Customs check. We had left the rear seat at home to make more room in the back of the car, and I put the wooden crate of food, the heaviest single item, in the floorwell over the axle. Behind this, and under the safari beds, I hid the shotguns in their leather case and the boxes of cartridges. Round the crate I stowed the expanding suitcase, the wicker-covered water-jar, the hamper of cooking utensils, the milk-can and the four biscuit tins full of coffee beans. Every remaining space was soon filled with parts of the cooking stove, the axe and the trowel, the bag of tent pegs, the collapsible washstand, and the small attaché-case which held the maps and the pocket dictionaries. On top of everything, bulging above the sides of the car, were the green canvas bath, the canvas bucket, the tent and the bedding rolled in a brown valise, which I lashed securely with a web of tightly knotted rope.

At eight-forty we lurched, wheels spinning, on to the road. We were still twelve miles from Dover, but I drove slowly at first, warming up the engine. A few minutes later we were overtaken by a motor cyclist with a girl on the pillion. Both the rider and his passenger were wearing rucksacks, and fixed below their number-plate was a black-and-white GB. They were travelling fast and swerved light-heartedly as they roared down the empty road.

"I bet they're going on our boat," Sibyl said.

I pressed my foot down on the accelerator, suddenly realising how much I should hate to miss the *Dinard*. The speedometer needle settled on seventy and the old car burbled and bucketed her way towards the coast.

In Dover we did our last-minute shopping, threw it hurriedly on to the tonneau cover and followed the clearly marked road to the dock.

The Customs man handed us the list of dutiable articles and we declared our wrist-watches.

"No camera?"

"No." That was what the coffee beans were for. When *The Wooden Horse* was published I'd promised Sibyl a camera, and good cameras were not easy to get in England in 1949. Currency restrictions for foreign travel were very much in force, and the French were short of coffee.

"What have you got in there?" He looked hopelessly at the overloaded car, the chocolate and paper bags of fruit on the furled hood.

"Camping kit. Tent, blankets, petrol stove, food . . ."

"How much food?"

"About thirty pounds."

The man grinned. "Excluding the weight of the tins, I suppose?" He marked crosses on the tyres with blue chalk. "OK —off you go."

Outside the Customs shed the sun was shining and white gulls screamed and swept low over the masts of the ferry. The sky was pale blue behind skeins of thin cloud, and the smell of sun on tarred wood became lost in the strong sick-making air that blew from the ventilators as we drove along the quay.

We stayed on deck, well forward with the wind in our faces,

and watched the spray breaking across the bows, sudden slaps of green that turned white when blown by the wind. I put my hands in my jacket pockets for warmth and found George's letter. I read it again to Sibyl. "*Coming with you part of the way. Crossing Dover-Calais. Meet us in Calais Monday morning. Lucille's never camped before and is a little nervous about insects. Also about latrine facilities. We shall manage all right, I hope, and not have to resort to going behind hedges*—that's from a man who fought the war in the Western Desert."

"I expect he's thinking of Lucille if she hasn't camped before."

I looked up from the letter at her solemn face. Her smooth brown skin which she never covers with makeup glowed warmly against the white paint of the lifeboat. "Listen to this," I said. "*Greatly look forward to the trip. Both fond of French cooking.*"

"That's what I mean. I hope they won't want to eat in restaurants."

"Oh no, I said that we were camping. They'll muck in all right." I leaned back in the slatted teak deck-chair and put my feet on the rail. George and I had first met in the crowd of ambitious young men who sought their fortune in a chain of vast retail stores. *There Is A Future In Management*, the Management had said in their *Times* advertisement—*for those who are prepared to start at the bottom.* George and I had started on the same day in the bargain basement, where University graduates rubbed shoulders with aspiring shop assistants in a ruthless struggle for promotion.

Sibyl was planning ahead. "How far will they come with us?"

"As far as Nice I should think. George has only got a fortnight and Lucille's bound to want to go to Paris."

By now we were approaching Boulogne with its damaged moles and half submerged wrecks, and the noise of concrete mixers and pneumatic drills came faintly across the water. Men were hard at work clearing the defences whose rusty iron shrapnel curtains still hung before the gun embrasures. On the wharf were knots of porters in faded blue overalls, and a row of English cars waiting to embark.

We had passports stamped, declared our currency, drew petrol coupons for a hundred litres and joined the queue of cars at the Customs check. The French were being very thorough, emptying every car, and I began to feel worried about the guns. The twenty-seven pounds of coffee beans were not important, but I did not want the guns impounded.

By the time we reached the head of the queue it seemed that the *douaniers* were tired. The tall thin one in a blue uniform looked at the tightly packed chattels under the tonneau cover and sighed. I lifted the bonnet and showed him the engine number, but he was not impressed. The RAC officer arrived with his assistant, a French youth in plus-fours and white socks.

"What's under here?" the RAC man asked.

"Camping kit." I began slowly to untie the intricate web of ropes which lashed the bundle down.

"Don't undo it." He turned to the douanier. "*Ils campent, ces gens-ci. Venez donc.*"

The douanier was not a man to be easily sidetracked. He began to pull fretfully at one corner of the tarpaulin.

"We're camping," I repeated loudly. "Tent, food!" I'd been through this so often as a prisoner that I thought I knew the drill. I made a show of struggling with the first knot, trying to show that although I was more than willing the operation was likely to take some time. But the Frenchman had more patience than the German guards and he watched dispassionately until I had released one corner of the groundsheet, then pushed me aside and fished out the suitcase.

Another douanier, this one short and fat, arrived. The tall one thrust the suitcase into his arms and pulled energetically at the tarpaulin that covered the rest of the luggage. The fat one rummaged among the contents of the case and discovered a jar of face cream. He held it up, reading proudly in English, "For the improvement of the skin." Sibyl complimented him on his accent, and he assured her that the cream was quite unnecessary. I decided she'd be able to handle him, and turned back to the thin douanier who had by this time removed the tarpaulin and was gazing in fury at the clutter of camp stools, beds and bits of petrol stove. I could see one brassbound corner of the guncase, which looked to me exactly what it was; and I almost wished that I had completed all the forms and brought the guns in legally. Then it had seemed an imposition to make it so difficult for a traveller to take his own property through Europe. Now, with all this uniformed power of international jealousy poking about among my private possessions, I began to see the point.

But the douanier was more interested in the big biscuit tins which held the coffee beans. He worried at one for a time, but it was held down by the weight of the crate of food. "That tin, what does it contain?"

"Nourishment," Sibyl told him. "We camp, you understand."

"Ah, you camp!" It was the fat one. He took the thin one by the arm and drew him away. "*Alors, m'sieur, m'dame, bonne promenade!*"

We fastened the tonneau cover and drove quickly through the barrier into the town.

Boulogne with its ruins, dust and temporary buildings was like Manila at the end of the war. There was the same devastation, the same brave improvisation with corrugated iron and composition board; but in Manila the flimsy shacks had been honky-tonks and Coca-cola saloons to cater for the American troops, while here they were genuine shops carrying on a useful trade. Sibyl bought food for lunch and we bumped slowly over the uneven *pavé* uphill away from the docks and out on to the Calais road.

I had forgotten to tighten the steering damper and the wheel kicked in my hands like a live thing, but I knew that a few minutes with a spanner when we stopped would make the steering on the heavy side, but solid and smooth.

The road to Calais ran along the edge of the sea. The beaches were fenced off with barbed wire and there were notices warning that the mines had not been cleared. Inland were huge concrete gun emplacements blasted by high explosives, their rusty iron reinforcement sticking out of the masonry like the ribs of a decomposing corpse. The whole area was bleak and seemed forgotten.

I turned off the road on to a narrow track which led to one of the forts. The ground was dry and chalky, scoured by the weather so that everything was clean and light in colour. We set up the table and the stools, and while Sibyl broke the long French loaf and spread it thickly with butter and garlic-smelling *pâté*, I poured the rough red wine. Away behind us, faintly, I could hear the sound of the sea on the beach.

We were still eating when a large American car came slowly towards us down the winding track and stopped with a jerk a few feet away. The youth who was driving, his father next to him, and his mother alone in the back seat, sat watching us.

"They're lucky," Sibyl said, "they've come just at feeding time."

I took a deep bite into an apple and read *United States Forces in Germany* on the number-plate of the car, wondering why, in all that vast desolation, they should have chosen just this spot.

Presently the front doors of the car opened and the two males backed out. Tall, loose-joined limbs, prep-school shirts, thin steel-grey tropical suits creased from sitting, crew haircuts and dark glasses; their only difference was in their ages. Each had a camera and an exposure meter in a little leather case. They advanced with determination towards the concrete fortification and began to take its photograph.

The two men had vanished from view into the redoubt. The woman in the car sat completely still. Perhaps, behind her spectacles, she slept.

The older man reappeared from behind the redoubt and came towards us. His son was still photographing—or using the building for some other purpose. The whole of the photography may have been an elaborate blind to cover this other, more personal, operation.

The older man stopped, and I broke the silence by wishing him good afternoon. He seemed astonished to hear English spoken, then embarrassed, as though he would rather it had never happened. "Say," he said, "I thought you were natives. Al fresco, eh? I was just about to ask you folk if I might take your picture."

"Have some wine first."

"Say, I'm sorry." The man backed hastily.

"It's not too bad—quite clean, I think."

"Sure, sure! But I guess I'd rather not."

There was a pause.

"Did you get some good photographs?" Sibyl asked. "The light's not good."

"This little machine takes care of that." He patted his Leica. "Say—this is a tre-mendous project. Tre-mendous. They tell me they're all the way along the coast. Fortifications."

"Rocket sites," Sibyl said.

"Say, is that so?"

"V2s," I said. "For a continuous bombardment of London."

"Say, is that right!"

"One a minute. We used to shoot them down as they came over."

"Say—have a cigar!" He took one from his jacket pocket.

"I didn't shoot any down myself."

"It's tre-mendous what you folk went through," the man said. "Tre-mendous. Yes, I'll say it was tre-mendous."

The younger man emerged from the redoubt and I offered him wine, but his father refused for him. "Junior's not touching it until he's twenty-one," he said, "then he'll be man enough to judge for himself." He turned to his son. "This gentleman here's been telling me that these are rocket-launching sites."

"I figured they were gun emplacements," the young man said. "For coastal defence."

"They're rocket-launching sites," the father said. "This gentleman says so, and he knows."

We watched the car climb tank-like back on to the road.

"They are gun emplacements, aren't they?" Sibyl said.

"Yes," I said, "for coastal defence."

The trees in the Bois de Licques were set far apart and the ground under them was free from scrub. At the edge of the wood was a large notice, faded by the weather: STATIONNEMENT DES NOMADES INTERDIT. I turned down one of the straight rides running at right angles to the road, and off this again on to the smooth ground at the foot of a tall beech; technically, we were not gypsies.

As I uncovered the back of the car I noticed the silence of the woods. At first it was a complete silence, no birds, no wind, no voices. Then I began to hear the rustle of the leaves in the high branches and faintly, in the distance, the sound of goat bells. While Sibyl unpacked the food hamper I took the small olive-green tent, still damp from the previous night, out of its canvas bag and set it up in front of the car where the ground was flat and covered with dry leaves, small twigs and the split brown husks of beechmast. I drove the pegs firmly into the soft earth and heard the blows echo through the woods.

I looked up to see a pair of large masculine boots topped by leather gaiters, above them dark cord breeches and a jacket of lighter cloth. The gamekeeper, he could have been nothing else, was carrying an ancient shotgun in one hand and from the other hung two dead rabbits. His face under the peaked cap was nut-brown, moustached, round and, at the moment, stern. He addressed me in French.

"He says we're not allowed to camp here," Sibyl said.

"Say it's our first night in France and we didn't know it was forbidden to camp."

She translated. "He says that if we camp here all the village will trespass and the owner wouldn't like it. It's a game preserve."

"Tell him that we'll leave first thing in the morning and respect the game."

She offered him tea and I fetched cigarettes from the car and invited him, in mime, to sit on one of the biscuit tins. He placed the rabbits and his old-fashioned hammer-gun carefully beside the tin on the ground, but before sitting down he made a short speech about the hospitality of France. Because we were English he would allow us to camp for the night, and we could obtain water from his cottage at the edge of the wood. He did not expect *monsieur le patron* down from Paris this weekend, but if he did arrive we were not to say that he, the *garde-chasse*, had given permission to camp.

All this he said directly to me, although by now he must have realised that whatever he said would have to be translated. I sat listening with my back against the smooth firm bark of the beech tree, noticing the difference in the tone of Sibyl's voice as she changed from one language to the other, pleased that I could understand some of the French which passed between them. The gamekeeper told us that we were camping near the site of the Field of the Cloth of Gold—he called it *le Camp du Drap d'Or*. There were still wild boar in the wood, he said, although most of them had been poached and eaten during the war. He talked of the expense of things and of how the young had forgotten what it is to work. It was the story we had heard often enough in England, but this time it was more remote and easier to understand. In a country that has deliberately 'gone slow' for years it is difficult to increase the tempo.

When the new black Citroën saloon came bumping gently down the ride, the gamekeeper went across to meet it. There was something crestfallen in the way he walked, and we guessed that this was the owner of the woods. The gamekeeper stood for some minutes, cap in hand, talking through the window of the car, and we sat tight, hoping that he was not in trouble, wondering whether we should have to pack and go. Then the driver, a plump youngish man wearing a beret, waved to us and smiled, and the Citroën lurched on down the ride. The gamekeeper also smiled as he came back. "That was *monsieur le patron*. You have the authorisation." With a grunt of satisfaction he took his seat on the biscuit tin and accepted another cup of tea.

CHAPTER TWO

DRIVING DOWN into Calais we thought the town had gone on strike, or that the Government was being overthrown. There were crowds in the streets, and an air of tense excitement. We drove between lines of waiting men and women and at every corner there was a police car with loudspeakers, or pairs of policemen on motor-cycles with revolvers at their belts.

On the outskirts of the docks we were stopped by a policeman who signalled us to the side of the road. "What's wrong?" Sibyl asked.

"Nothing is wrong, madame, it is the *Tour de France*."

Then the cyclists came past, each team wearing brightly coloured caps and racing singlets. There were supply cars behind them laden with spare wheels, first-aid kit and team managers in plus-fours standing on the running-boards or sitting crosslegged on the roof, with anxious responsible expressions on their faces.

Once clear of the bicycles I drove as fast as the pavé would allow. The roads inland had not been good, but these in Calais were little better than they had been on D-day. An hour late we clattered down the main road leading to the docks.

"Bill! Bill!"

I drew in to the kerb. There was George, tall and English-looking in his tweed jacket and grey flannel trousers, collar and tie. Lucille, tall and slim and also in tweeds, was standing by his side.

"Sorry we're late," I said. "We got caught up in a bicycle race."

"That's all right, Lucille's been shopping."

"Already?"

"Only window-shopping. She's been pricing things—it'll be days before she gets down to buying. The only thing we need at the moment is bread, then we're ready for the great adventure."

"We've got some bread," Sibyl told him.

"You've brought the old crock I see."

"I can't get rid of her," I said, "she follows me around."

"No, I mean the car—I really can't think what you want with a thing like that. I should have thought you'd have bought the latest model, all the money you've made."

"We don't get the money," I said. "I'm only an agent for the Government. Did you have a good crossing?"

"Pretty good. Lucille was sick all the way. Where do we go from here?"

"We've got to collect more petrol coupons. We thought we'd blitz south as hard as we can and draw them in Dijon."

"Don't we go through Paris?" Lucille said.

"Well no. . . . You see, there's a good main road across the Alps straight to the Riviera. We thought we'd lose no time up here in the north, but get to the sun as soon as possible."

"I think you're right," George said. He turned to Lucille. "Look, we'll come through Paris on the way home and if we've any money left we'll spend it there."

"Good," I said. "Who's leading?"

"I've got to call at a garage first." George was embarrassed. "There's something wrong with the electrical side."

I looked at the gleaming American-style convertible which stood by the kerb. The hood and windows were operated by electricity. "D'you mean you can't open it?"

"Well, that's better than not being able to close it."

"Much worse," Sibyl said firmly.

"Won't the radio or the heater work either?"

"Not at the moment." George sounded huffed.

"What a journey you must have had."

From Calais we drove back to Boulogne and then slowly on the pavé until we reached the long straight tree-lined roads on which I love to drive. We had left Amiens and Abbeville far behind before we stopped for lunch in a small unfenced orchard sloping gently from the road.

"I'll brew up," George said.

"Before lunch?"

"Easy to see you weren't in the desert. Always brew up as soon as you stop, that's the drill." He got out his primus stove and set the kettle boiling. "Now tell me what it's all about. As soon as I heard you two were driving down to the Riviera I was in on it like a shot. Too good a thing to miss. But what's it all about, I mean what are you going to do when you get up to Germany?"

I had been wondering exactly this for the last few weeks. Lewis's had given me six months' leave so that I could help in making a film of my escape from Germany. Half that time had already gone in writing the script and interviewing actors for the principal parts; but what I was to do on location had never been explained. "Oh, we shall just hang around while they shoot the film, I expect."

"And Sibyl's going as your secretary, I suppose." He lay stretched on the grass in the warm sun, a steaming cup of tea at his elbow, and from the way he said it you would have thought I was taking her round the world on a luxury cruise at the Company's expense.

"Of course."

"Where are you making it exactly?"

"Luneburg Heath. You know, where the Germans surrendered to Montgomery." We had flown out there in the spring to find the right location. The Army were lending us part of an artillery range and digging out some authentic German huts and plenty of barbed wire. They'd promised us if we were still there in the autumn they'd give us some real shooting. "There are thousands of acres lifting with game, and the Germans aren't allowed to have guns."

"I can see what sort of shooting you're going to do," George said. "You don't look as though you've been burning much midnight oil, either of you. You look as though you've just come back from the South of France."

"We held our script conferences in the garden." I thought of the country house near the film studio where we had stayed as guests of the film director, and the sunny terrace where we'd sometimes spent a whole morning over one passage of dialogue. I thought of the freedom of those long spring days when I was doing what I wanted to do instead of what I had to do, while George sat in the small office in London watching the sun filter dustily through a window of reeded glass. I remembered Strauss, the Merchandise Manager, and his show of temper on the floor one lovely morning in March. Sunlight streaming in through the high windows had prompted the girl in charge of Ladies' Hats to put on a Spring Display and little Strauss, after a night in the train, had stamped about screaming, "Spring is not 'ere! Spring is not 'ere! *I* will tell you when ze spring is 'ere!"

George broke into my thoughts. "You'll never go back, not

now you've tasted blood. . . . Although it's not a bad firm. They were pretty good after the war, there was none of that nonsense of finding someone else in your job."

"That was good business sense," Sibyl said.

"I shall never forget, soon after I got back——" George seemed in no hurry to get on the road again. "I was very conscious of the fact that the old man was now a lord. He came to Manchester to give us a pep talk because, owing to the war, discipline had got a bit slack. All the managers were assembled very solemnly in the boardroom. There was the usual psychological pause and then he came in, all stately in a black jacket and striped trousers, with that magnificent head of his just slightly on one side—you know how he does. He told us enough of the economic state of the country to make us feel that we'd all been wasting our time in the Forces, and then started in on the discipline angle. He drew himself up to his full height, looked slowly around the room and said, 'You must remember, gentlemen, a fear of the Lord is a healthy thing.' Thinking it was a jolly good pun, I let out a loud guffaw which rang round the boardroom like a trump in church."

I could imagine it only too well. Even though the successful years had mellowed the character and tempered the ruthlessness they had not made the great man any less frightening. Korda had been the same when I had met him over the film deal. The initial bargaining had been left to his executives, who had been empowered to give way, to indulge my inexperienced feinting and attempts to play one company against the other, so that the first offer of five hundred pounds had become a firm contract for ten thousand. But Korda himself had not had to give way. He had appeared at the end, with the soft voice and the paternal hand on the upper arm, all the little relaxed mannerisms of the man who has arrived. It is only those who have got there, or have been there all the time, who can afford benignity; but scratch the surface and you'll find the steel all right. "What did he do?" I asked.

"He ignored me," George said. "I tried to turn the laugh into a cough, and nearly choked myself and had to leave the room. . . . I was never going back, after the war. It's funny how quickly you toe the line when you're demobbed."

Yes, I thought, I wasn't going back either, after the war. It was something we'd all discussed time and again; in the crewroom at night, waiting to take off on a raid, and in the prison camp—especially in the prison camp where we'd had so much time for working things out. None of us who were employed by big Organisations were ever going back. We all did though, all who survived.

A peasant on a white carthorse passed, silhouetted against the blue sky. He was a young man, browned by the weather, and he looked down on us and wished us *bon voyage*.

"That's the life," George said. "I bet he doesn't worry about consumer characteristics."

"You'd be bored to death in a week," Lucille told him.

"Not me, I wouldn't mind being a farmer. Then I could grow a beard—what is it, Bill, a badge of independence?"

"In a way," I said. Or was shaving a badge of servitude? You don't grow a beard after all, you shave one off.

"You'll have to shave it off before you come back."

"I think it suits him," Lucille said. "It makes him look like Ernest Hemingway."

"Good-looking chap, Hemingway," Sibyl said. "Good writer too."

"He's deeply symbolic, isn't he," Lucille said, "under that toughness?"

"We're all deeply symbolic in one way or another," I said. "This beard could be the symbol of a long-suppressed wish to avoid shaving."

When we were in the car again, driving down the long straight road, Sibyl said, "I've never understood exactly why you did go back after the war. I was surprised when you did."

"There were several reasons. They'd always been very good to me. They made up my salary when I was in the ranks, when I first joined the RAF, so that I was able to pay Mother her allowance even as an AC2, and I sort of owed it to them to go back, at first, at any rate."

"They might just as well have paid you the money as give it up in profits tax. It wasn't charity." She had worked for a big organisation too.

"That's the point. It was a sort of retainer and one was more or less obliged to go back. Then when I saw the Managing Director he told me about the special promotion scheme they'd worked out for us. And later when they made me book-buyer it was exciting in a way, and I was working too damned hard learning how to do it to think of independence. . . . I'm just old enough to remember what happened to all those chaps who started off as chicken farmers after the First World War. Most of them finished up selling matches in the street or hawking brushes from door to door—and they'd had capital. It was the only job I knew, and being aircrew doesn't exactly fit you for a job except a permanent commission or in an air line, and I was too old for either. . . . Buying books has its advantages. You get plenty of reading matter."

"It's bad for your health," she said, "to sit behind a desk all day—buying books."

We drove fast all that afternoon, determined to get as far south as possible before making camp. We passed through the narrow cobbled streets of Coucy-le-Chateau, cool and dark between ancient buildings with steeply pitched roofs and towers; out again into the bright sunshine, over the Ailette and the Oise canal, and then down a steep winding road cut into the side of the hill, zigzagging down in a series of hairpin bends, turning back on itself, separated from the slopes by a low stone wall. Looking upwards from the valley of the Aisne we could see this cream wall cutting zigzag up the face of the hill, crumbling, spilling honeysuckle from cracks and crevices, surmounted by tall towers warm against the sky. On through Soissons with its ancient abbey and ruined cathedral, Chateau-Thierry where we crossed the Marne, and Sézanne whose streets were lined with mountain-ash, a lovely rose-emblazoned town. Every mile was taking us farther south, to the hot sunshine of the Mediterranean, the red earth, the blue sea and the pines.

We stopped at a small peasant farm set well back from the road, a huddle of mean buildings with the living cottage smaller and less cared-for than the barn. Sibyl and I took the two milk-cans and squelched across the muddy yard. We were greeted by calves, ducks, geese and hens, and a small girl who said she would call *maman*. We heard her shouts diminishing as she ran through the house and down the lane.

We waited for half an hour. I was all for moving on but Sibyl, reluctant to waste in vain time already wasted, wanted to stay. Then the woman came, thin wispy grey hair, long black apron over a shapeless brown frock, hurrying in her clogs, flustered by this strange intrusion. Yes, she would be willing to sell milk, she seemed eager to do so. Calling a cow in from the field she hastily swilled a bucket in doubtful water, fetched a stool from the kitchen and, seizing the cow, dragged it into a dark and smelly byre.

When she had finished she led us, milk slopping over the rim of the bucket on to the muck-strewn mud of the yard, into a kitchen dark as the byre. She reached proudly for a strainer hanging on the wall but, finding it dirty, she sent her daughter for another. The child returned empty-handed, so the mother shrugged and used the dirty one. I thought of the hospital cleanliness of the kitchen at home, but Sibyl did not seem to mind.

All the time the woman was working she talked. Not able to understand the fast French I looked round the simple kitchen, at the bare wooden table, the hard earth floor at which the hens were pecking, the black iron stove.

The deal was finished and Sibyl was saying goodbye. The woman turned to me and said, "*Au revoir*, *m'sieur*." I made the effort and bowed. "*Bon soir*, *madame*." She turned back to Sibyl and asked a question, but I caught only the word *écrivain* in her reply.

"What was she talking about?" I asked as we picked our way back towards the cars, each holding a can of the warm fresh milk.

"Mostly about her organs. She's got a dropped womb and she said most of the farmers' wives get it after about the seventh child and working in the fields. She was rather sweet, very envious of our holiday but in a nice way. She said she'd always wanted to see the Mediterranean but she'd never been farther than the market town.'"

"The milk didn't look too clean to me."

"Oh, I'll boil it, otherwise it won't keep."

"What was she saying about me, by the way?"

"She wanted to know what you did for a living."

"What did you say?"

"Nothing."

"You did! I heard you say I was a writer."

"She asked me first if you were an artist and I said no, a writer. Then she asked if you wrote love stories."

"What did you tell her?"

"I told her you didn't have to. I said that love stories were written by people who loved only in their imagination."

"What did you really say?"

"I just said no. Then she asked if you wrote detective

novels, and I said no. And she said, what did you write about then? So I told her that you wrote about life, and she said, 'Ah, life, that's very difficult.'"

I wondered why she hadn't told the farmer's wife that I was a book-buyer. I knew the difficulty. If she'd said I was a bookseller she'd have been understood, but a book-buyer, one-sided product of vast retail organisation, meant nothing to anyone who was not in the trade. After all, everyone was a book-buyer in his own small way, or nearly everyone. She could have said that I was a bookseller which, although not strictly true, would have been easily understood. I grinned, acknowledging her refusal to acknowledge a status she regarded as merely temporary.

We had decided to camp beside the river; it was Tuesday and we had last bathed on Sunday morning. On the map the river and a canal ran side by side not far beyond Méry-sur-Seine and so we found them, with the road, now an embankment, crossing both by a narrow bridge. The low-lying land between the river and the canal was waterlogged, and I drew up and waited for the others to arrive.

"This is no good. Too many mosquitoes." The sun had set and George had already changed into khaki drill trousers and a long-sleeved shirt.

"It looks pretty grim I agree, but I doubt if there are any mosquitoes. Gnats, more likely."

"We'd better decide on a place soon," Lucille said. "It's nearly dark."

"We said we were going to camp early." George sounded tired.

Sibyl called to a woman who came past on a bicycle. She wobbled to a standstill several yards away and repeated in a shrill voice, "Dress the tent, madame? Here? But the mosquitoes! . . ."

We turned the cars with difficulty on the narrow causeway and drove back to the main road. It was quite dark now, and after a few miles we turned off on to the edge of a field of stubble.

CHAPTER THREE

THE ALARM clock rang at five and I sat up to turn it off. Sibyl began to mutter sleepily.

"What's that?"

She opened her eyes slowly, reluctantly. "Oh I was dreaming that I was aboard a pirate ship. . . ."

"What were you doing, walking the plank?"

"No, they were friendly pirates." She fell asleep again.

I lay for some time in the warm sleeping-bag, looking through the mosquito-curtain at the front mudguard of the car and half the green canvas bucket leaning against the wheel. Sibyl slept quietly. Quietly confident. She had told the woman at the farm that I was a writer—as though you could call yourself a writer with one book to your credit. She was all for me leaving Lewis's and trying to live by writing, but all my training, all my inherited sense of values were urging me to stay where I was. I had always belonged to some big organisation or another; first school, then Lewis's, then the RAF—and Lewis's again. I could go right through my life belonging. I could keep my present job and comfortable salary and write another book in my spare time. You'll never do it, she had said. If you stay on you'll never write another book worth reading. And I knew that she was right.

What was she doing now, with her pirates? She had the heart of a boy in the body of a girl—probably leading a boarding party. How she enjoyed this sort of holiday, and how lucky I was that she did. The next three weeks spread themselves out before me free of care and interruption; moving on, always moving, sleeping and breaking camp and moving on. I could do it for ever. Especially after those other mornings, hundreds of other mornings, when I had lain in my warm sleeping-bag and the only moving on had been by inches scraped laboriously in the dark earth, and the only horizon had been paralleled with barbed wire. But that was finished now. I had been lucky to escape, lucky to meet Sibyl, and now luck had brought me success as an author and the chance to make my book into a film. For the next three weeks we would relax.

I crawled out of the tent. The mist was dispersing, leaving a thin film of shining dew. The cars were wet with dew and the tarpaulin was cold and stiff in my hands as I took it from the bonnet of the car. I spread the tarpaulin dry side up on the damp stubble. The other, light-green tent was closed and silent, but the undulations of our own olive-green canvas told me that Sibyl was dressing. I took the petrol stove from the back of the car and as I was lighting it she joined me. "Get out of my kitchen," she said.

I left the stove to her, and rigged the spare groundsheet between the two cars to make a bathroom. By now George was greeting the morning noisily, grumbling about the mosquitoes. Even up here, away from the river, they had been active.

In the first village I stopped by a petrol pump on the left of the road, so that Sibyl was next to the kerb. "Try them with coffee beans and see what happens."

"How much shall I offer?"

"Leave it to them. Order the petrol, and while they're putting it in tell them you've got some coffee beans and ask if they'd rather have that than money."

A woman came, and I sat there, trying to follow the conversation. It had been the same in Germany when we were on the run and only Mike could speak the language. I'd had to hold back then. I had wanted to get on with it, but knew that I would only ball things up if I spoke. That had been a strain and now, sitting in the car in the warm sun, I had something of the same feeling of frustration. But the discussion did not last long, and Sibyl took one of the tins of coffee beans into the shop. When she came back the woman and a man were with her, and all three were smiling. The man opened the door of the car and bowed, and they both stood waving until we were out of sight.

"How did it go?"

"They were delighted. They said they hadn't seen so much coffee for years. She suggested twenty litres a kilo, so I told her to fill the tank."

"We'll look for that camera in Dijon," I said.

We stopped outside the town to change our clothes. Sibyl replaced her loose red cotton shirt and faded blue jeans with a white frock printed with a design by Fougasse, and as she transformed herself into a cool sophisticated young woman I thought how pleasant it was to be married to so many different people all at once. The other car swept past and stopped with a squeal of brakes. "Anything wrong?" George shouted.

"No, just changing."

"OK. Catch us up."

We overtook them on the outskirts of Dijon. George was standing beside the car, a look of wonder on his face. I pulled up. "Anything wrong?"

"No, I've just bought some petrol. I gave them a kilo of coffee and they gave me twenty litres—and fifty francs into the bargain."

"If they gave you fifty francs change," Sibyl calculated, "that means a kilo of coffee must be worth at least six hundred francs. No wonder the people in the last garage seemed well satisfied."

"We'll go to a café and you can do a deal with the proprietor," I told her. "He's bound to be in the black market. But we'll buy the camera first."

"Lucille wants to do some shopping, so we'll meet you in an hour in the main square," George said. "Don't clinch the deal before we come."

We saw the camera we wanted in a shop window. It was priced at thirty-five thousand francs which represented a few pounds less than our combined capital in French currency. "Come on," I said, "we've still got most of the coffee beans. We're about five hundred miles from the Italian border. We can just about make it and buy a couple of rolls of film as well."

"Supposing the car breaks down?"

"The car won't break down."

"Quickly, touch some wood."

The camera was a German Retina and the shopkeeper told us that it had been smuggled into France via Switzerland. "It is a fine make," he said, "and very difficult to find in France."

"Impossible in England."

"It is incredible," the man said. "They tell us that Germany lost the war, yet an Englishman has to come to France to buy a camera smuggled from Germany."

When we left the shop Sibyl had the camera slung from its leather strap across her shoulder. "Now I need a drink," I said.

"Can we afford it?"

"I feel sick. I always feel sick when I've spent a lot of money. We need a drink."

"It's a lovely camera. Thank you very much."

"It was an investment. You take care of it."

We went to the nearest café, where comfortable wicker chairs stood in the blue shade of a gaily striped awning, and ordered Dubonnet. Everyone else in the town seemed to have gone to bed. The air in the streets was shimmering and the sun had drawn the colour from the brighter objects, leaving white light and deep shade in vivid contrast. Under the awning it was cool, the pavement damp from water sprinkled by a languid waiter. I saw George and Lucille walking slowly down the street in the high sun. George was wearing an unbelted bush jacket which fell almost to the bottom of his thin white shorts. His face was red, but his legs and arms were brown. Lucille looked cool in a silk blouse and white skirt. She stopped at a shop window while George, obviously bored with window-gazing, stood in the shadow of the doorway lighting a cigarette. Lucille called him and he joined her at the window.

"What about the coffee beans?" I wanted to get it done.

"I'll speak to the waitress in a minute." Sibyl was playing with the camera.

"What's the good of asking the waitress? Ask to see the proprietor."

"I'll ask the waitress first. Her boy friend might be on the black market."

"The proprietor's sure to be."

George saw us from across the road, he spoke to Lucille and they came over. "You haven't sold the coffee yet?"

"Not yet. We're going to ask the waitress when we order your drinks. What'll you have?"

"Something long and cool please. I shouldn't think you'd get much joy here. Anyway I should ask the proprietor, not a waitress."

"It's just the place," I said. "They need bags of coffee in a joint like this. We got the camera."

"So I noticed. Did you get an instruction book with it?"

"They hadn't one, but he showed us how it works."

"There's a lot can go wrong with a camera like that." George looked at the lens. "F2. I never use anything bigger than F8 myself."

When the waitress brought the drinks Sibyl said, "We have coffee to sell. Would *monsieur lè propriètaire* wish to buy some?"

The waitress did not seem surprised. She asked how many kilos, and the price. Sibyl told her ten kilos and that she wanted eight hundred francs the kilo. After a few minutes the waitress came back and said the patron would not pay more than six hundred francs the kilo. Sibyl told her that she regretted, but eight hundred francs was the price. The waitress also regretted and withdrew.

"That's that," I said. "Six hundred francs seems to be the price."

"I'm not so sure. Let's hang on for a bit longer."

George called the waitress and repeated the order. When the girl returned she whispered in Sibyl's ear. She looked at me. "He's offering seven hundred."

"Take it." I wanted to be done with it, hating this bargaining through her but knowing that I could never do it with my French. "Seven hundred isn't bad."

"We'll sell ours too," George said. "Might as well get it all done in one fell swoop. Then I shan't have to do any more bargaining."

It was hot out in the sun, like walking into an oven. The heat hit us in the face and burned through the soles of our shoes. The metal of the cars was too hot to touch and the sun beat back from the canvas as I took off the tonneau cover. We unpacked watched by a crowd of small boys who gathered quickly from nowhere and did not seem to feel the heat. The coffee beans were at the bottom, and the boys kept up an incessant clamour for chewing-gum. In vain George told them that we were British, not American; in vain he tried to dismiss them in his unequivocal Cairo-Arabic, they craved gum and would not be convinced. Feeling certain that they would take the matter into their own hands as soon as our backs were turned, I persuaded Lucille to guard the cars while we went back with the coffee beans.

As we entered the dim cool interior of the cafè a man rose from a table by the wall where he had been lunching with his family and took us in silence into a small dark pantry in the rear. We stumbled after him, watched by his wife and family of round-eyed children. I led the procession with one of the large tins, followed by Sibyl clutching one of the small tins and George who sweated under his entire stock. No caravan bearing exotic spices from the East could have been watched with more silent wonder.

The man stood on one side for us to enter, then locked the door. He was tall, thin and stooping and wore horn-rimmed spectacles. He did not speak, but he was obviously used to this sort of transaction and motioned us to put the tins down on a rough wooden bench which stood against the wall.

"There is more coffee than I offered at first," Sibyl told him. "I have seven kilos and *monsieur* here has nine kilos more. But the weight is not exact and I should be glad if you would weigh it."

The patron pursed his thick lips. "The coffee, is it ground?"

"But no, *monsieur*. It is grilled, but not ground."

He grunted, and left through a second door leading out on to the yard.

"Taciturn individual."

"He's furious that we raised the price."

"Hope he hasn't gone for the police," George said.

But the man came back with an old-fashioned set of scales. He placed them on the wooden bench and watched as I removed the strips of gummed paper which had sealed the tins, releasing a fragrant bouquet which reminded me of the shop in Mortimer Street and the polite astonishment of the man behind the counter when we had walked in with four empty biscuit tins and asked him to fill them with coffee.

The patron seized one of the tins and poured a shining cascade of brown beans on to the scales. The aroma increased, pungent, filling the small room. He could scarcely conceal his excitement.

"It is good coffee, eh, *monsieur*?"

"It is not bad, *madame*. Of course you understand that one brings coffee here from Switzerland. Dijon is not far from the frontier. But it is not bad coffee this. I am paying a high enough price for it." In sulky silence he finished the weighing and calculated the cost. It came to eleven thousand two hundred francs exactly, and he paid us out of the till in the front of the café. Once the money had changed hands he became more agreeable. He asked where we were going, and enthused about the Mediterranean coast. He complimented Sibyl on her business acumen and on her French, ignoring George and me as being mere porters. Still chatting amiably to Sibyl, he accompanied us to the door and stood there watching as we walked across the burning square. Conscious of the scrutiny, I wondered who had come better out of the deal.

The road was long and straight and white in front of us and the elms that lined it were tall and gave but little shade. On our right were the low hills of the Côte d'Or and on our left, but farther away, the high white peaks of the Jura mountains. Between us and the cool hills lay row after row of closely planted vines, orderly, groomed, without shade, separated from the upper pasture and the road by low stone walls almost the colour of the earth. We drove for longer than we had intended because there was no shade, no relief from the blue sky that poured down such vibrant heat, the road that shimmered before our eyes, the horizon that danced and merged the road into the sky. I pulled up at last under a tree slightly thicker than the others and sat gratefully in its shade. I heard George draw up behind, but lacked the energy to look. Then I heard a car door slam and his footsteps on the road.

"About time you stopped."

"I'm sorry, George, I couldn't see any shade."

After lunch Sibyl made coffee, and an old man working in a narrow field of potatoes raised his head and scented the air. He came slowly across and stood above us on the road, saying nothing. "*Bonjour, monsieur,*" I said. I've noticed that people who stammer are always talkative; whether this is to reassure themselves, or whether it stems from a characteristic obstinacy, a determination to conquer the damned thing, I don't know. In my case it has led me to acquire a facility in greeting in several European languages, which gives an entirely misleading impression of my fluency. Now, as usual, the old man's long and fast reply was above my head. I turned to Sibyl.

"He wants to know where we come from and whether we're visiting the vineyards and he hopes we enjoyed our food in the open air."

"Ask him if he'd like some coffee."

He smiled, and his face softened. He removed his hard black hat and climbed carefully down the slight embankment. I rose to help him, feeling his arm light and brittle beneath the thin stuff of his cotton shirt. He sat carefully on the edge of the bedroll, put his stick on the ground and replaced his hat. Light blue eyes in a wrinkled network of red skin regarded me steadily from above a white moustache which almost completely hid his mouth.

"Ask him if it's going to rain." As she translated I pointed to the heavy-looking cumulus cloud which hung above the mountains on our left.

"But no, *monsieur*," the old man replied soothingly. "It is always there, that cloud. The mountain would look strange without her cloud. But it does not portend rain here in the valley."

He sat for some time without drinking, a frail old man in a clean collarless shirt with full narrow-cuffed sleeves, a stiff black waistcoat, narrow hard masculine trousers and wooden clogs. A powder of white stubble softened the outline of his jaw. He seemed lost in reverie, or too shy to talk; or perhaps the coffee was too hot. The hands that held the mug were large and square, moving continually with the tremor of old age. He put the mug beside him on the ground, as though to drink too soon would shorten the pleasure, and I offered him a cigarette which he treated as a choice cigar, holding it between finger and thumb, drawing on it gently and not inhaling.

He drank the coffee slowly and wiped his moustache with his hand. "It is many months since I have tasted coffee. It is now almost June and we have not yet drawn our ration for March. I cannot afford to buy it on the black market."

"How much does one pay on the black market?" Sibyl asked.

"One pays a thousand francs the kilo, *madame*. It is formidable."

She looked across at me and grinned. "A thousand francs the kilo."

I thought of the proprietor grumbling over his bargain at seven hundred francs. He had not done so badly after all. "Hear that, George? A thousand francs the kilo down here."

"I still think I did the right thing," George said. "I like to turn my stock over."

Sibyl was listening to the old man, who had lost his shyness and was speaking too fast for me to understand. She translated. "He's a pensioner. He lives in one room and can't live on his pension. He's eighty-three and still has to work. Shall we give him some coffee beans?"

"At a thousand francs the kilo?" I went to the car and began to fill a paper bag from one of the remaining tins.

"What about camping early tonight?" George said.

"I was just thinking the same thing. We won't stop for tea, we'll push straight on, camp early and have a good supper."

"I feel as though I haven't slept for weeks," Lucille said.

Back in the shade the old man had started on his second mug of coffee and was telling Sibyl the history of the château which stood away from the road, among the vines. Once the château had been privately owned. Those were the good days. There was much entertaining and an Englishman used to come and stay. Now it was owned by a company and no one lived there. Times were different now. Money no longer bought anything, and old-age pensioners must work.

"This old-age pensioner isn't working very hard. He's been here an hour already. It's time we were moving." I began to pack the car.

The old man climbed slowly to his feet, removed his hat and thanked us for our hospitality. I gave him the paper bag and he took it with him across the road to the potato field. We were ready to move off when he called to Sibyl. He had something in his hand.

"What is it?" I asked.

"A colorado beetle."

The old man squashed the beetle between his finger and thumb. "There are thousands of these among the potatoes. They ruin the crop. But what can one do?" It was additional evidence that things were not the same.

I had almost given up hope of camping before dark when we came to a narrow col where the road crossed a mountain stream which, pale green, twisted and tumbled whitely on its stony bed. There was a grass shelf to the left of the road, a jutting balcony with an unrestricted view of the snow-streaked nakedness of the Massif du Pelvoux across the valley. It was a quiet place, dominated by the towering Alps, wild and rocky, but warm now in the rose-coloured light of the evening sun. The country here was olive-green and brown, dappled with splashes of sunlight but grey-blue in the shadows.

We turned off the main road down a rutted track which, doubling back on itself, ran parallel to the road about twenty feet below it and stopped abruptly at the edge of the gorge over which the road was carried. Still lower, but unapproachable by car, was the ledge of grass, and a thousand feet below this was the valley with its toylike houses and tiny fields.

"I thought we were camping early," George said.

"We've been looking," I told him, "but it's always the same. Whenever you want to camp you're not in camping country. We'll take it easier tomorrow."

He put up his tent in silence, at the side of the road near the cars, and we took ours down to the strip of grass where we pitched it a few feet from the sheer drop to the rushing stream. Behind us a waterfall cascaded into the gorge, and I noticed a horizontal ledge about eight feet from the top of the waterfall and a traverse in the rock along which we could reach the ledge. It was a perfect natural shower-bath.

The water was ice-cold and fell with such force that I had to cover my head with my arms. I stood under the fall, feeling it wash away the strain and sweat of travel, leaving me cool and ready for the meal Sibyl was cooking. And as I dried myself in the sun, the stone ledge warm under my feet, I remembered the banks of open showers and the emaciated men with leather skins who had stood under them, in Manila. I remembered the warm quiet privacy of the shower at mid-day when the newly-released prisoners were eating and I, hot and sticky after the morning interviews, had come down to take my second bath. The concrete at that time of the day had been almost too hot to stand on, and the water cold by comparison. I would stand there letting the water run down my back, drying myself in the sun, and then put on a khaki bush shirt freshly laundered by a woman in the village and smelling faintly of the dry clean odour of rice-starch. Back in the open-sided mess hut with the flyscreens up and the concrete floor cool and watered, we would drink the American iced tea with lemon out of mess-tins that were fogged with dew on the outside. By the time we had eaten we would be hot and sticky again. In the afternoon I would go down to the hospital with its thatched roof and woven palm walls open top and bottom, its strong smell of antiseptic which failed to drown the sickly sweet stench that came from the open sores of the men who had been prisoners of the Japanese. They lay in rows down each wall of the hut, rows of shrunken skull-like faces, heads shaven, in each face large hungry eyes deep-sunken in their sockets, trunks and limbs emaciated or swollen with beri-beri, distended bellies, arms and legs no thicker than cricket stumps. I would stop at each bed, call each man by his name, ask after his health, give him news of friends in camp. Some would be recovering, eager to get away; others, still in the coma that had clouded the last days of their captivity, would slowly turn their unreflecting eyes, frightened to come out of the dream in which they now believed themselves.

I had done what I could. Redundant aircrew at the end of the war had been two a penny, you saw them everywhere; young men with large moustaches and wings above a row of frayed ribbon on the breasts of their tunics, struggling with accounts, stores, administration. I had chosen Welfare as perhaps the least boring, the most entertaining way of finishing a war. I had not found it entertaining.

We heard the hard and hollow-sounding bells long before we saw the herd of dun-coloured cows sway slowly up the road. They were driven by a wild-looking girl with bare brown legs, who flourished a long stick and uttered weird harsh cries as she sent her dog barking at the heels of a straying cow.

"I'll see if we can get some milk." Sibyl climbed the embankment and walked across to the girl whose dog, a woolly creature as wild-looking as his owner, kept the cows in a huddle at the side of the road. She called down for the milk cans, and I collected Lucille's and took them up to her on the road.

"Ask her if there's an *estaminet* near here." George was obviously tired and I thought it might cheer him up to have a drink.

The girl said there was one in Monestier, the nearest village, but when Sibyl asked her if she thought the cars would be safe she replied that the local people would never steal but there were strangers on the road who would take anything. Had she not been taking the cows home she would have been pleased to stay and guard the encampment, but things being so she would wish us goodnight and return with the milk at six in the morning.

We drank wine with George and Lucille instead of going in search of the estaminet. We were all tired and pleasantly mellow after the meal and the heat of the day.

"Why are some wines red and others white?" Lucille asked. "Is it that they're made from red and white grapes?"

"It's the skin," I told her. "If they leave the skin of the grape in during fermentation the wine is red, but if only the pulp is used it's white."

"It's a bit more complicated than that, I think," Sibyl said.

"Yes, but that's the rough idea. I wonder who first thought of fermenting grape juice to make wine."

"I suppose it was discovered by accident, like most things," George said. "I made some by accident myself when I was in Palestine."

"Not again!" Lucille said. "I thought we'd finished with Palestine."

George pretended not to hear. "Oddly enough we were riding through Cana, where Christ performed the water into wine miracle. I bought a large bunch of grapes from a wog, put them in my mess-tin and forgot all about them. The movement of my horse and the heat must have started fermentation, because the next day I had a mess-tin half full of wine."

"What a war," I said. "Horses and wine."

"You'd have had them if you'd stayed in the Yeomanry," George said. "But no, you wanted wings."

I sat drinking the rough red wine from the metal tumbler and pondered on the chain of lucky coincidences that we call careers. If, way back in 1935, I hadn't decided not to sign on for another four years in the Yeomanry I wouldn't be here now, with Sibyl, on our way to make a film in Germany.

"Was it really wine or just grape juice?" Sibyl asked George.

"Well, it was hardly champagne, but it was a bit more than grape juice."

I would probably never have met Sibyl anyway, and if it hadn't been for her I would never have written the book which was the mainspring of it all.

"I've always wondered how they get the bubbles in champagne," Lucille said.

"You'd have been much better off with us," George told me. "We were a unit, and we stayed as a unit."

The Yeomanry had been fun at first and well worth the hours of polishing rusty bright spurs and pipeclaying sword belts for the riding and the mock battles in Windsor Great Park, where we spent our training periods riding the Guards' horses and sleeping in their barracks. But, later, hunting on Punch and duckshooting in the marshes, the thrill of being mobile in my own car, had filled all my spare time; and even the War Office had realised that cavalry would be of little use in another war—except in the desert. The Corporal-major had summed it up nicely: "Now, a pair of you have been sent out on reconnaissance. What d'you do? You ride careful, keeping to low ground, and when you get to the foot of the ridge one of you stays below to hold the horses, see? You don't just tie the reins together and both go up. One stays below, as horse-holder. Then the bloke that's going up creeps up careful, keeps 'is head down, see? And peers over the top. He takes a careful note of the dispensation of the forces—the way they're armed. Try to get a fair idea of the numbers—then crawl down again, careful. Remember what you saw. Don't come back to me at a split-arse gallop and say, 'Coo, corporal, there ain't 'arf a flippin' lot of 'em!'"

"Do you know how they get the bubbles in champagne?" Lucille was talking to Sibyl.

"They're caused by the wine fermenting after it's been bottled. That's why the cork's wired on, and flies off with such a pop."

The morning war was declared I'd called at the Depôt to rejoin but had been told, amid the bustle of preparation and the stamping of horses' feet, that I could no longer join a regiment; I must join the army. That had been the end of soldiering for me. I had thought the matter over and decided on the RAF. At the age of twenty-eight, and by then a Sales Manager, I had gone to school again to learn navigation with a crowd of youngsters in their teens.

"Do you think you'll come back to Lewis's," George said, "after all this?"

"I don't know. I haven't made up my mind yet."

"You'd be a fool not to. You've got your feet well on the ladder now."

"I'm not all that sure I want to climb it."

"Will you write another book, d'you think?"

"That's what I don't know."

A car roared above us on the Route Nationale, gilding the top of the tent with light as it passed.

"This is the life," George said. "We used to have nights like this in the desert, nights when the stars burned like candles and the moon looked so low you could pluck it with your hand. I often think I could write a book myself."

Lucille drew her collar close round her throat and shuddered. "There's that sand blowing in again." She laughed. "I always tease him about it, but I'd love to go to the Middle East if it wasn't for the insects."

"Insects!" I said. "You wait till you get to the Riviera. Read that bit out of the old Cook's Guide, darling."

Sibyl read by the light of the headlamps. "'The information given in this book has been compiled chiefly for the benefit of persons visiting the Riviera to recruit or preserve delicate health, or those who, having ample time and money at their disposal, leave their own country in the search of perpetual summer and perpetual gaiety. . . .'"

"That's you," George said, "your life's one long holiday."

The low clear voice went on. "'The Riviera is, however, full of interest to students of botany, geology, entomology and ichthyology . . .'"

"That's Lucille."

"'Not only are the cloudless skies, the warm sun and the beautiful scenery of the Riviera towns—Cannes, Nice, and Menton—inducements for migration to escape the English winter, but as yet the English holiday tourist has not penetrated so far, and consequently the surrounding country, with its pine woods, its orange and myrtle groves, is open to all, and the traveller may explore the neighbourhood with a freedom almost unknown at home.'"

"Read that bit about the frogs," I told her.

"'But if there are no birds to sing among the branches of the trees,'" Sybil continued, "'their places are fully occupied by the green frogs which all day long lie concealed among the friendly coloured leaves, and only make their presence known when twilight succeeds the day; then the chorus begins, and through the length and breadth of the Riviera a fearful croaking prevails, and lasts throughout the night.'"

"It's not true," Lucille said. "You're making it up."

We were in the tent and I had to shout to be heard above the roar of the waterfall. "Why doesn't Lucille like George to talk about the war?"

"It's because she was at home all the time I expect. The war must have been pretty boring for her, he didn't come home at all for five years."

"All the more reason for her to want to hear about it, I should have thought."

"Maybe she'd rather forget the years they weren't together. I think some want to hear all about it and so share it, others would rather ignore it. It's an awful long time to be apart."

I remembered Catchpole, my first 'case' in the hospital in Manila; a big man, his once ruddy face a shrunken mask. When he spoke his voice was quiet, dead. "I want to stop the allowance to my wife." At the foot of the bed was a card: AC H. Catchpole, R.G., RAF. Age 26—and then some medical data. He looked about sixty.

"Tell me all about it," I had said. "Perhaps I can help." It was the professional patter of the Welfare Officer.

The letter he had handed me, pathetic in its mis-spelling, laboriously written, had told in hackneyed phrases of his parents' joy at his deliverance, becoming angry only towards the end as it told of his wife's infidelity. I had read it several times, wondering what to say. Why couldn't they have waited until the man was home. I thought of the young wife, lonely, without news for years that her husband was even alive. *She's out all night with soldiers*, the mother had said.

"Why not leave it until you get home?" I said it not to shirk responsibility, but because I knew how impossible it was to advise another's course of conduct. My job, as I saw it, was to keep them as happy as I could while they were in the transit camp, but some of them wanted everything solved. They had not been allowed to make decisions or accept responsibility for so long that they had lost the power. "See her," I urged, "and hear the story from her own lips."

"I never want to see her again." Catchpole had choked, and turned away his head, slowly, miserably. "I want my allowance stopped." It was the only redress available.

"If I send a cable today the allowance can't be stopped until seven weeks after the Air Ministry get the message, that's the Regulations. You'll be nearly home by then. Why not let it lie until you've thought it over, until you're fit again? There may be some mistake. You don't want to do anything you may regret. Why not see her first and talk it over?"

Catchpole had only turned away again, stubborn now that the Welfare Officer had refused to ease him of his burden; and I had sat by the bed, feeling my impotence, my inability to help. I thought of the padre but dismissed the idea. *Whom*

God hath joined let no man put asunder. . . . How useless, how utterly pathetically useless. I racked my brains for something adequate to say. What could you do after all, to help a man? A man could only help himself. There was too much interference in other people's affairs, far too many chaps setting themselves up as gods with the ability to straighten out another man's life. Look at the psychiatrists in the RAF. They claimed they could judge a man's suitability for aircrew. They had devised a test which was supposed to tell, infallibly, how a man would react over the target when he was blinded by searchlights and deafened by exploding flak. My squadron had sent four of its experienced crews, my own included, to test the test—and every man had failed. I thought of Roger. He had been worried that he was not getting all he should from married life. Or was it that they couldn't make children, or that his wife was a bit unsettled? I couldn't remember for the moment, but it was nothing they couldn't have straightened out themselves. Roger had gone to a psychiatrist and the man had put him on a couch; and from that moment his life was ruined. It appeared it was all his mother's fault for bringing him up wrongly as a child. He had quarrelled with his mother, he and his wife had parted, and now they were all unhappy; and all because that damned quack had given him someone else to blame instead of letting him work out his own salvation.

Catchpole was in a bad way, and the most I could do was to persuade him to wait until he was strong enough to tackle it. But tackle it he must, there could be no shifting it on to someone else.

"Try to puzzle it out," I'd said. "I was a prisoner in Germany——" (they always took you more seriously when they heard that). "There was a chap in my room who heard that his wife had been killed in England by a bomb. He felt like hell about it at first, didn't care what happened. Then he began to see that all grieving is really selfishness, he was grieving for his own loss, sorry for himself. He realised that death must come to everyone and that it's those who are left behind who suffer. I know your case is different—but try to look at it as though your wife were dead. . . . Is it she you grieve for, or the mess it's making of your life? If it's the blow to your pride then you must stop being sorry for yourself, and get a divorce and start again. It's bloody hard I know, but try to decide exactly what it is that hurts you. Is it the thought of life without her or the injury that she's done you? Think it over. I'll be round again tomorrow. I'll leave the question of the allowance for the moment, shall I?" And I had left him lying like a living skeleton under his thin sheet; recovered from the Japanese, but at the same time dealt a blow more difficult to counter because the battle must be fought alone and in the last analysis the decision must be his.

CHAPTER FOUR

THE SUN rising over the Massif threw long shadows across the valley. The sky was warm above the mountain range but the warmth had not yet reached the ledge where we were camped. The waterfall was numbing in its coldness, and after my shower I wore a heavy woollen sweater while I stood guard for Sibyl to take her bath. Her naked body was pale brown and smooth against the rough dark rock, and I watched the play of light and shade, the rise and fall of rounded buttocks, as she felt her way along the narrow ledge until she stood, breasts cradled in one arm, testing the water with her hand. She shouted something but, warm now in my sweater, I shook my head and waved her on. She grimaced and with her head shielded by her clasped hands huddled under the fall of icy water.

The cow girl came with the milk and I paid her the forty francs. She was driving her cows and goats down to a sloping field on the other side of the road, and I invited her in basic French to come back in half an hour for coffee. She asked where madame was and I told her. "*Elle se baigne.*" She nodded, as though I had misunderstood the question and it wasn't worth pursuing the matter.

She came back as we were finishing breakfast. She was shy at first, but told us that her name was Tatiane, that she was twenty and that she lived in a single-roomed cottage with her mother and father and brother. The cows were not theirs but belonged to the farm which lay back off the road. She drank the coffee with such noisy enjoyment that Sibyl gave her one of the tins which we had brought for our personal use.

After breakfast I fetched buckets of water and washed the car. Sibyl scrubbed some clothes on the smooth white stones of the river, kneeling in the bright sunshine shaded by her big-brimmed straw hat. Tatiane hovered nearby, watching us and going at intervals to watch George who was wrestling with the electrical apparatus of his car, and to take a look at the cows penned in their field by her dog which she had told us was a griffon. It was obvious that strangers were an exciting novelty to her. She must have had some experience of the army because she kept asking for tins of *bullybif*. We told her that such things were rationed in England but either she did not understand or she would not believe, for she reiterated her demands for 'bif' and also for jam and sugar.

The clothes dried quickly in the sun and at ten o'clock we began to strike camp. Sibyl had nearly packed when she missed a blouse which she treasured because it could be slipped from her shoulders for sunbathing in the car. "I know I left it on the front seat," she insisted. "I was going to change into it before we left."

"You must have packed it in with the washing," I said. "I haven't put the suitcase away yet."

"I know I didn't." But she looked through it for form's sake. "It isn't here."

"We must have dropped it out then—unless it's fallen down behind the seat."

"I think Tatiane's taken it."

"Surely not. What would she want with a thing like that?"

"She was hanging round the car most of the time, and you left it for a few minutes each time you went for water."

"She was just interested in us, that's all. She's just a simple peasant girl."

"Simple peasant girls are sometimes thieves."

"Well, you can't do much about it." I looked at Tatiane, now some distance down the road, sitting on a rock in the shadow of a tree at the edge of a field of newly cut hay, her arms folded across her stick, her legs swinging in studied nonchalance. I thought perhaps Sibyl was right, but realised the difficulty of our position. "If she took it she's hidden it by now. We'll just have to cut our losses and be more careful in the future. Lucky she didn't take the camera."

But Sibyl never recognises a difficult position. She took her handbag from the seat of the car, and I caught the fringe of her suspicion as she looked inside. "That settles it," she said. "All the money's gone. I'm going to get it back."

I went over to George, who was ready for the road, and told him what had happened.

"All these French peasants are decadent," he said. "Just like the wogs. I wouldn't trust one of 'em."

"You said this one had pretty legs," Lucille reminded him.

"That's beside the point. That has nothing to do with her morals." He looked at me. "Come on, we'd better go down and lend our support."

The girl was still sitting in the shade and Sibyl was standing on the road in the sun. Their voices came faintly on the mountain air, Sibyl's low and controlled, the girl's rising quickly to a crescendo of denial, becoming hard in challenge.

Dressed in shorts and espadrilles we walked self-consciously down the road. There was a light of battle in Sibyl's eye. "I know she's got it. Do you think you could frighten her?"

I tried to look stern but no doubt contrived only to look sheepish. George adopted his air of a respectable citizen attending a slightly unpleasant road accident. Sibyl spoke again to the girl, and I heard the word *gendarme* repeated several times.

The girl was defiant, and I understood her reply. "If you bring the gendarme he will do—what?"

"I'll tell her you're going to search the field," Sibyl said. "I believe she's got it hidden in the hay." She spoke to the girl, who became violent again and brandished her stick in the air. "I thought so—she's getting windy now. She says it's a private field and you've no right to go into it. Just pretend you're going to search."

I looked at the four-acre field covered with loose hay and wondered how I was supposed to pretend to search it. "Come on, George," We walked slowly side by side up one edge of the field, kicking over the hay with our feet as we went. Tatiane ran to the middle of the field and toyed with a dangerous-looking pitchfork while Sibyl, separated from us by a ditch, watched her from the road.

We completed four unproductive beats of the field. "This is stalemate," I said. "I'll just look along the ditch, although I really think it's useless." I jumped down into the ditch and began to turn over the long grass which fringed its brink. The sun was hot on my naked back and the scent of the newly cut grass was sweet and strong.

Sibyl called excitedly. "Look! She's got something white there!"

I straightened and saw the girl standing one hand on her hip, beckoning with the other. "*Venez donc!*" she screamed. "*Venez voir!*"

We crossed the field to where she was standing. At her feet

was a small heap of clothing, half hidden by the hay. Sibyl picked up her favourite blouse, and with it a Jacqumar scarf I had given her for Christmas and a pair of pale pink panties which could only be Lucille's.

We left Tatiane turning the hay, pretending to ignore us, and went back to Lucille. "We've got a pair of your pants," Sibyl told her with some satisfaction. "You'd better check up and see that nothing else is gone."

"How can I check—there's so much stuff." Lucille looked helplessly at the baggage. "How can I tell if anything's missing out of that lot?"

A flock of sheep slithered down the path, chased by a boy of about fourteen who was wearing a large straw hat and smoking a cigarette. He carried a handful of stones with which he pelted the sheep to keep them on the move. "That girl up there," George told him, "she is a thief." The boy looked at us with upward slanting eyes, boldly; shrugged his shoulders and went on down the track.

"The money! We didn't get the money back!" Sibyl ran after Tatiane, who had left the hayfield and was driving her cows up a narrow path between low stone walls.

I overtook them both before the girl had reached the farm, in a small dell by the side of the stream, overshadowed by a rocky bluff. She was carrying a bundle tied with a white cloth and as we came up with her she backed against the wall of rock.

Sibyl challenged her. "And the money, mademoiselle? What have you done with the money?"

The girl groped in the pocket of her grey denim overall and pulled out a roll of notes which she offered without speaking.

"I wonder what else she's got?" Sibyl said.

"She can't have much else. Let's get back to the car."

"And what else, mademoiselle?" she asked her.

"*Rien! Rien du tout!*" The girl was suddenly indignant at this further suspicion. With a swift movement she ripped open the front of her overall and stood naked to the waist, revealing her white, rather dirty, smallish breasts. "*Rien!*" she shouted again. "*Rien du tout!*"

"What is in that bundle?" Sibyl asked.

The girl buttoned up her overall and untied the bundle, squatting on the ground. She held up the contents one by one; a piece of cheese, a grubby handkerchief, the forty francs

I had paid her for the milk, and the tin of coffee, the chocolate, cigarettes and soap we had given her that morning. "These are mine," she said sullenly. "Madame *gave* them to me."

"You're going to the police of course," Lucille said.
"Why?" Sibyl was surprised.
"To lay a charge."
"We've got the stuff back," I said.
"That's not the point. She'll probably steal from other cars."
That will be between them and Tatiane, I thought.
"It was my fault really," Sibyl said, "for leaving so much stuff lying around. To a girl like that we must have seemed like millionaires."
"The police wouldn't do anything anyway," George said.
"That's not the point. It's your duty to go." Lucille climbed into the car. "You haven't an ounce of public spirit among the lot of you."
It was an anti-climax when their car refused to start. The prolonged use of the headlamps the previous night had overtaxed the battery and the starter motor was completely dead. There was not even enough life in the battery to give a spark when the engine was turned by hand. Watched by the sardonic-faced boy in the straw hat we manhandled the car on to the road and pushed it for a hundred yards before the engine fired.
"Did you notice Lucille's face when she recognised her pants?" I said as we walked back to the Bentley.
"They were rather gorgeous—I think they were the ones she bought in Dijon."
"Reminds me of the Liverpool store. We had a young lad just down from Oxford where he'd been reading law. He'd decided to go into Trade instead. He'd been given part of the furniture department to look after and they'd had a consignment of cheap chests of drawers—thousands of 'em. The manager sent for him and said, 'This is a very good line, now go and think up a slogan to persuade people they ought to have a chest of drawers. I want them all sold by Saturday night.' We'd just had escalators built in the store, they were probably the first in Liverpool and they were strange and rather frightening to some of the customers. The slogan this chap thought up and plastered right across the foot of one of the escalators was

Drawers Are Necessary. . . . Soon after that they moved him into Ladies' Underwear. He was the chap who launched the *Go To The Flickers In Celanese Knickers* campaign."

"What's he doing now—General Manager or something?"

I sat there warming up the engine. "No, he was killed at Arnhem."

We climbed into a wild rocky pass where the mountain fields were studded with wild flowers and gridded with wooden snow fences, and then followed the River Buech in its headlong course down the southern watershed. Here the river was swift and ran impetuously green and white through a narrow chalky gorge where a gypsy family had halted on a muddy stretch of ground at the side of the road. Behind them was a rocky football pitch with rickety goalposts, where the gypsies' assorted herd of goats, asses and sheep was grazing. We stopped, and Sibyl photographed the goalkeeper, a ram with a baleful eye. All the animals were long-haired and wild-looking, and the donkeys, thick-necked and warmly coated, were lovable as they had been on the sands of Margate when I was a boy. The air was filled with the scent of lavender which seemed to grow from the rock itself, so thin was the soil in which it had its root.

Later we stopped to eat lunch in the shade of an almond tree beside the fast-moving river, and watched a thunderstorm build up behind the mountaintops. The storm caught us in the next village but I drove on through a deluge of rain, obstinately refusing to raise the hood, until we got so wet that we were compelled to stop. George passed laughing while we were drying ourselves with difficulty in the car, and we caught him up in Serres with its tall houses huddled together in ancient cubist pattern on the rocky slopes.

Coming down a sharp hill into a valley where the road ran alongside the railway we saw three cows being driven by a girl and a boy. I stopped suddenly, and heard George braking hard behind. "Is it possible to buy milk?" Sibyl called.

"No, not possible!" the boy shouted.

"Wait, I go to find madame." The girl smiled and drove her hesitant suspicious cow past the cars to a house on the opposite side of the road. A woman appeared on the first floor balcony and came heavily down the outside stairs, her wooden sabots scraping as she walked. If we would wait while the boy milked a cow she would be pleased to sell us milk.

We followed her into the warm byre which occupied the whole ground floor of the house and when Sibyl told her that she too could milk they talked farming, while the boy spurted milk viciously into his bucket and the girl smiled in quiet triumph from the corner stall. I wondered whether I should ever have the capital to buy her the farm she wanted. My favourite aunt's criterion of a wealthy man was one who had so much money he didn't know what he was worth, and I had never thought that this would ever be applied to me. The book had now earned me in royalties and film rights a round sum of twenty thousand pounds. The figure took my breath away each time I thought of it, but all of it had come in one year and more than fifteen thousand pounds would go in income tax. If my father had left me twenty thousand pounds I should have paid about two thousand five hundred in death duties and the rest would have been mine, but because I had earned the money I must be happy with something less than a quarter of it; and happy I was, but it would not buy a farm. Even if the book sold phenomenally for the rest of the year and brought me forty thousand pounds, there would still be less than five thousand when tax had been deducted.

Now that we had milk we thought of camping, but the road was hemmed in between the railway and the river and it was again late when I at last stopped the car, at a point where the old road had been abandoned and a new straight causeway made nearer to the railway. The old road, its tarmac cracked and washed clean by the winter snow, wound out towards the river and stopped abruptly at the bank as though it had been blown up or washed away.

I tested the old tarmac with my heel and found that the weather had not softened it enough to take the tent pegs. Casting round for large stones to anchor the tent on the hard surface I noticed that down below, right on the river's edge, was a still older road, little more than a track, almost overgrown with brambles and covered with short grass, completely hidden from the modern causeway along which traffic was continually passing. I walked quickly back to Sibyl who had unpacked the hamper and started the petrol stove. "What about going down there—we can have a bath before breakfast."

"Oh, this place seems all right to me."

"But it's much nicer down there. It's another perfect camping spot."

She laughed. "We're only staying the night, not building a house. We can go for a bath in the morning."

"It'll save climbing down and getting hot climbing up again. Besides the car got filthy in that storm and we can wash it in the morning."

She walked to the edge of the tarmac road and looked down on to the track below. "Can we make it?"

"I'll back down, there's not room to turn at the bottom. What about it, George?"

"We'll stay up here," George said. "I've promised myself an early night."

I could smell the thyme and aniseed crushed by the wheels as I backed down the steeply sloping ramp. There were white boulders in the bed of the river, which was strongly flowing and cold as ice. I saw the signs left by other campers, the barely discernible traces of the considerate traveller; the small heap of harmless ash where rubbish had been burned, away from the site, and the freshly turned earth where the non-combustible rubbish had been buried. Dozens of us could camp here in succession and still leave it clean and beautiful for those who follow. I had a feeling of warm friendship for those earlier unknown campers.

By the time the tent was up and the beds laid out Sibyl had fried the steak over the stove on the running-board of the car. The last light was fading and I lashed the electric torch to the windscreen. We ate sleepily, the air filled with the sharp throbbing music of the cicadas in the rough grass and the rushing tumble of the river.

CHAPTER FIVE

I AWOKE TO the sound of men's voices and the revving engine of a car. It was not yet light but the headlamps shone through the canvas of the tent. At first I thought that the shouts were directed at us, in anger, then as I became more fully awake I realised that the strange car was stuck on the sloping track down to the lower road.

"Eh, Pablo!" One of the voices was nearer than the others. "A little to the right and she will come! To the right, Pablo, to the right—there is plenty of room!"

There was more frenzied revving of the engine, then the sound of rending metal and the clatter of a small avalanche of stones tumbling down the embankment.

"Now she marches! To the right, to the right!" And again the horrible scraping sound of metal on jagged stone. I could not understand Pablo's reply to his guide, but he did not sound pleased.

At last, in spite of the conflicting advice, encouragement and recrimination in four male voices, the car was free, and I watched the light inside the tent grow brighter as they edged on down the track, shouting as they came. They'll have to get out backwards, I thought, but I suppose that's better than backing down in the dark. But what is it that gives them this warmth so early in the morning? Is it the wine they drink? I tried to imagine a party of Englishmen with a car stuck on a tricky slope above a river bank at three in the morning darkness.

The car stopped right outside the tent. There was some muttering and giggling, and four car doors slammed loudly one by one. "Silence! You will wake them!" a voice shouted. There was a great scuffling and dragging of heavy objects, and the four doors slammed again. Lying in the darkness of the tent, I wondered what was happening now. Judging by the excitement in the voices and what little of the conversation I could understand, it seemed that the Frenchmen were embarking on some sort of outing. That was it—they were going fishing.

I lay listening to the muttering and clicking as rods were fitted together, and the loud discussion of who would fish where. I imagined from their voices four comfortable middle-aged shopkeepers, elaborately equipped with wicker baskets full of food and wine, having left their wives warm in bed, braving the early morning darkness; the intrepid, their morning made for them by the fact that we the foreigners were, they congratulated themselves, fast asleep in our green tent while they set out to face nature in the raw. At length the party moved off to the accompaniment of the most fruity voice complaining, "*Pablo! Eh, Pablo! Ou est mon anorak?*"

When I awoke again it was daylight. I thrust my head from the tent. Parked close by, so close that it seemed to be nuzzling the flank of the Bentley, was an old black Citroën; out in midstream, as far apart as they could possibly be, four solitary figures were perched precariously on their individual rocks. Each figure held a long rod, and at his side was a fair-sized hamper.

I placed a finger to Sibyl's lips. "Sh-h, be as quiet as you can. We're surrounded."

"By what?" she whispered.

"Stick your head out and you'll see."

She wriggled out of her sleeping-bag and crawled on hands and knees to the entrance of the tent. "How did they get there?"

"Under cover of darkness. I've handed out the last of the ammunition. You know the Colonel's dead?"

"I'll just run up the flag," she said. "Then I'll cook breakfast. They won't look so many on a full stomach."

The morning bath in the river was impossible. It was not that we feared the outraged susceptibilities of the French, it was the soap. Two of the fishermen were downstream and I could not face the flood of protest that such pollution of the water would undoubtedly release. We fetched buckets of the cold clear water and washed in the canvas bath inside the tent.

George's battery was dead again and as we pushed him to start the engine on the slightly sloping old road I saw the wisdom in his not going down to the river bank. "How will you cope on the way back?" I said.

"We'll have to camp on hills, that's all. Then we can get a rolling start."

"Or stay at hotels to save the battery." Lucille sounded hopeful.

"There won't be any money left for Paris if we do that."

"What's wrong with it?" I asked. "I thought that chap in Calais had fixed it."

"It's the whole bag of tricks." George gazed at the car with something like hatred. "My old Austin never gave me a moment's trouble. This thing's been back to the Works more than it's been on the road. I collected it myself to make certain they didn't towse it on the way up—and the gearbox seized up solid through lack of oil after a hundred miles. I had to get it towed. The factory manager said it couldn't happen. I showed him the receipt from the chap who'd towed me and filled the gearbox with oil, and he still wouldn't believe it—said that every car goes through ten checks before it leaves the Works. But they gave me a new gearbox eventually, and a hundred miles after that I ran a front wheel bearing. They blamed that on the five o'clock shift. Apparently these chaps have so many bearings to assemble in a day and if it's getting near five o'clock and they haven't done their quota they assemble 'em without grease to save time. I suggested sacking 'em but he said all the rest would go on strike."

"Did they give you a new bearing?"

"Oh yes. Then one of the springs broke."

"You should get something like this," I said. "Goes on for ever."

"You're a reactionary," George said, "living in the past."

That may be true. She was the first Bentley built by Rolls-Royce, in 1933, and I had paid nearly as much for her in 1949 as she had cost when new. Solid and dependable, built by hand of the best materials, her brakes and roadholding are equal to her speed. She is long and low and to watch her drive away you get the same kick in your heart as you do to see a sleek boat, close hauled, cutting through the water. Driving her you feel the wind in your face and the nature of the road in your hands and by putting her at the corners you can leave a softly sprung modern car, tyres squealing, far behind.

We followed the river up into the hills, climbing between high cliffs of black rock with the river, now a trickle, on our right hand. At intervals along the bank were large notices in red, DANGER DE MORT, giving warning that the level of the river was subject to sudden fluctuation. At the top was a huge hydro-electric station whose concrete dam held back the water in a deep blue lake. As we stopped to wait for George, the lock gates were opened to release a flood of water which roared and thrashed its way thunderously down the valley. I thought of the lonely fishermen on their rocks and wondered how much of the flood would be dissipated before it reached them. Visions of the imprecation and panic as the four scrambled to safety in the face of the oncoming flood kept us amused for miles.

The road beyond the pass clung to the face of the mountains, a serpentine road that turned back on itself so completely that sometimes the two cars were travelling parallel to one another but in opposite directions. Occasionally we would hear the sad wailing note of a horn several bends ahead and a great motor coach full of sleeping passengers would come swaying towards us, holding the crown of the road, veering out dangerously at the turns and passing in a cloud of dust and noise.

Then it was downhill all the way until we saw the multi-coloured and sharply pitched roofs of Castellane which, from above, was like a fairy town with pointed towers and crenellated walls dominated by a tall pinnacle of rock on which stood a chapel half hidden by trees. The town was as lovely as its introduction, with narrow streets converging on to a sunny market-place surrounded by tall trees. A band of gypsies with their travelling fair was drawn up in the centre and their gaudy caravans were bright against the sandy floor of the square.

I sat in the car while Sibyl bought the food for the day. A great blue coach on its way from Nice to Grenoble had pulled into the square and I watched as its passengers struggled free and made for one of the cafés and the pissoir which stood outside the post office. The top of the coach was piled high with bicycles, every passenger was loaded with luggage and provisions, and everyone was in holiday mood. The older people were dressed in black, but the girls wore cotton skirts and white blouses and the young men brightly coloured sweat shirts, diminutive shorts and linen caps. After ten minutes the driver, who had been smoking a cigarette in the shadow of his coach, climbed into his seat and sounded a long blast on the bugle-like horn. Slowly his flock of passengers assembled. There was much discussion punctuated by repeated blasts of the horn until at last everyone was rounded up and squeezed in; and with elbows and shoulders bulging from every window the blue monster rattled away over the mountains towards Grenoble, its strident horn fading into the distance. All was again peaceful in the square.

There it goes, I thought, a coachload of humanity. If I were a novelist I should be weaving a story; appreciating, inferring, deducing, commenting. But I can only write about myself and what I know—and that's little enough. Most people, I suppose, try to write at least one book. My father was always at it, full of ideas but not a single one was carried through. As a boy I had tried to write a novel in the manner of Eric Linklater with a dash of Aldous Huxley. It was called *The Complete Man* and was designed to show how when released from his inhibitions by alcohol the normal civilised man could be as happy as the savage. There was plenty of free love in it too, and no one did any work. . . . And now a critic had praised *The Wooden Horse* by saying that the green mantle of John Buchan could descend upon my shoulders. It had done me a lot of good with my publisher; but I know my weakness. As the eldest of five children I would sit with the others in the upstairs room we called the playroom and cudgel my brains as they asked me for a story. Not only was I unable to invent even the simplest tale, but the plots of the stories I had read had vanished from my mind. I could remember vividly scenes, emotions, sights and sounds, but I could never report 'what happened next'. I could remember the wounded trapper lighting a fire to keep the wolves at bay as the implacable Arctic darkness descended on a featureless waste of snow, I could hear the ice cracking like a pistol shot and—faint but growing nearer—the eerie howling of the wolves. I shivered with the trapper when I saw the double points of fire reflected in the eyes of the surrounding beasts, and I smelled the awful rankness as they crept nearer when the fire died down. As the circle tightened I would throw a burning brand, and the circle would widen again; but there was one brand less, and I knew that the fire would not outlast the night. What I did not know, what I do not know to this day, is whether the man was saved or eaten. To me it is unimportant. I have lived that night, and the author probably did not know what it feels like to be eaten.

Nice, with its pseudo-Oriental and stucco hotels and boarding-houses, had the atmosphere of Brighton at the height of the season (or perhaps I was tired after driving all day in the hot sun). Even the palms, set among deck-chairs, coloured umbrellas, teeming pedestrians and parked cars, looked jaded. The sea was undeniably blue and the sun was shining, but the sea was confined by concrete, fringed by a myriad sprawling forms, and the light of the sun was filtered by exhaust smoke.

We turned off the Promenade des Anglais along which antiquated carriages on narrow rubber tyres bowled silently behind sway-backed horses, and into the Avenue Félix-Faure where we at last found space to park the cars. Lucille, snared by the window displays, pleaded for an hour's shopping. George had a headache and preferred to stay in the car, in the shade.

We found a small square in the old part of the town where the people were content to sit quietly in the shadow of their tall houses. There was a fountain close at hand whose plashing stream of water arched cleanly into a dark stone pool, and I filled the water jar ready for the night's camp. "We'll find somewhere quieter in Italy," I said. "We shall be crossing the border tomorrow."

"We've still got about ten kilos of coffee left. I hope we get through the Customs with it." She seemed doubtful.

"I'm more concerned about the guns. But I agree we'd be better off without the coffee."

"Let's sell the lot!" She made it sound an adventure. "We're bound to get a good price here, everyone's rolling in money."

"Right—then we'll be able to fill up with petrol before we go into Italy."

I sat in the car while Sibyl, looking a typical *niçoise* with her sun-warmed skin and brightly coloured dress and faded espadrilles, went to look for a grocer's shop. Opposite, a long flight of hollow uneven steps led crookedly up the hill above the docks. The golden sun of early evening fell slanting across the steps and on the level platforms between the flights men in their shirtsleeves sat on wooden chairs. At the top a group of girls in flame-coloured kimonos chattered outside a darkly beaded doorway. Occasionally, hand in hand or with twined arms, they would run up or down the steps to stop poised like butterflies against the peeling plaster walls.

I waited for half an hour and when Sibyl did not return I thought that perhaps we had mistaken one another and had agreed to meet with the others outside the Casino. I drove to the Casino, but there was no one waiting. When I got back to the square she was standing by the kerb talking to a man who wore a linen cap, an open-necked shirt and narrow-legged check trousers, low-waisted and tight across the hips. She introduced us in French, and we shook hands. He was about my height, wiry, smooth-skinned, and his light brown eyes looked up and down the street as he spoke.

"He's offering us eight hundred francs a kilo," she said. "His brother-in-law has a shop in a side street here."

I handed over the two biscuit tins. The man tucked them under his arms and set off with Sibyl down an alley so narrow that cars could not drive through it and the upper storeys of the high houses almost met overhead.

"Don't be long," I called, not liking the look of the man and wishing that I could have gone instead. I cursed the language difficulty that made it necessary for her to do the job that I should have been doing, and walked impatiently up and down, the camera slung over my shoulder, keeping a wary eye on the car. Two gypsies were arguing over a pitch at the bottom of the steps. They both had large baskets of blood-red, pink and white carnations, and the owner of the pitch, a girl of about nineteen who carried a baby on her hip, had arrived to find the other, older woman had occupied her place. She had set up her basket at the foot of the steps and was nervously arranging her flowers in sudden patches of contrasting colour, splashing them with beads of water from a tin, while the younger gypsy stood off and appealed to the crowd which included two gendarmes who kept slightly aloof, smoking. Then the girl parked her basket by the wall, hoisted the baby to her shoulder and, patting a rapid unconscious accompaniment on its back, began to scream invective. What she said I had no idea, Sibyl would probably not have understood. It was in patois, or perhaps even Romany; but it was certainly effective. A group of swarthy men gathered round her, gypsies, and on the older woman's side a crowd of lighter coloured, more urban men. I began to doubt that the older woman was a gypsy after all. She was dark, but she may have been from the town.

The young girl was crying. Her greasy black hair fell in ropey coils from a head that was lifted in objurgation, and now the light wailing cries of the child were added to those of its angry mother. A crowd of the kimonoed girls from the house at the top of the steps stood, arms entwined, obviously siding with the gypsy. She appealed to them, dramatically pointing first to the basket of flowers, next to her pitch occupied by the interloper. She spat, all the time monotonously patting the child's back and rocking to and fro on her feet to soothe it. The swarthy men surged forward as though to eject the older woman by force, but at last the gendarmes intervened and took the girl away.

I waited for another hour but Sibyl did not come. I went back to the car and sat fretting wondering what had become of her. Perhaps she had been caught by the police selling black market coffee. Or drugged and carried off to a brothel. I remembered stories I had heard of dark men with hypodermic needles in Oxford Street, of young girls vanishing never to be heard of again. I forced my mind back to less nightmarish thoughts. We were half an hour overdue to meet George and Lucille who I knew would be waiting outside the Casino, but I was reluctant to go to them in case she came back while I was away.

I was trying to work out in French what I would say to the police when an old man with a cloth cap pulled low over a wine-reddened face shuffled up and thrust a note into my hand. It was from Sibyl, written on the back of an old envelope. *Darling*, I read, *Don't worry—I've got to wait for the money. Suggest you collect the others and come back to the square. I'll be as quick as I can.*

"Where is madame?" I asked.

The man did not understand, but tapped the note and nodded his head in reassurance.

I scrambled out of the car and grabbed his arm. With my free hand I pointed at his chest. "*Vous*," I said, and pointed to myself, "*Moi*," and then down the alley, "*Madame!*" He understood and shuffled off.

I followed, gripping the camera firmly in my hand and leaving the rest to fate. The old man led me up the narrow passage, where dark-eyed Moorish-looking men lounged in doorways or passed silently by on rope-soled feet, through steeply climbing streets of tall houses close together with slatted wooden shutters from which washing hung to dry. Only a few yards behind the busy boulevard, this labyrinth of twisting passages and crooked steps was part of a different world where the fears of my imagination were the normal events of life. I was already lost and followed my guide blindly, thinking only of Sibyl and wishing I had never let her go. Damn the car and all its contents. I wanted to find her, to take her away into the safety of the open countryside.

She was sitting in a long dark estaminet at a round wooden table, and when she saw me she tried to smile. There were several men standing at the bar and they looked round with curiosity as I entered. "What are you doing here?"

"Oh darling, please buy me a drink."

I crossed the sawdust-covered floor to the *zinc* and ordered two vin rouge from the sharp-eyed woman behind it. I took them back to the table. "Why the hell didn't you let me know where you were?" I had been frightened and now I was not frightened any more I was angry.

She looked worried and unhappy. "I've done an awful thing."

"Well?"

"I'm afraid I've lost the coffee."

"Lost the coffee! How?"

"That man said he'd get me a thousand francs the kilo, and he went off with it and he's never come back."

"D'you mean to tell me that you let that fellow go off with it without paying you first?"

"Yes—he said he'd come back."

"Come on. We've had that coffee."

"Do you really think so?"

"I'm sure of it. Come on—drink up!" I got to my feet.

"I'd like to wait a bit longer."

"Come on! There's no point in waiting. Besides there's no one looking after the car."

"Please let me wait."

I could see that she meant it, that she was determined to wait, and I thought that she would be safe enough in the bar. "I'll go and fetch the others and get them to stay with the car while I come back for you. But stay here. I won't be long."

I walked quickly back to the car, losing my way twice in that maze of narrow streets, expecting to find it ransacked. But it was untouched, secure and very English-looking with its GB plate and wire wheels. I collected George and Lucille from outside the Casino and without wasting any time in explanation asked them to keep an eye on the Bentley while I went for Sibyl.

The men in the bar stopped talking when they saw me, and

stood watching. I was certain that they were in the thing, that they knew everything that had happened. She was sitting at the table, writing in her diary, and it was obvious from her face that the man had not come back. "It's no use," I said. "We might as well call it a day."

"I've had another vin rouge." She said it like a small girl.

I paid for the wine and followed her out into the street. "Now tell me what happened."

She looked happier now she was in the open air and I remembered how she hated confined places. "I asked a grocer if he wanted any coffee, and he said he'd pay eight hundred francs. So I offered him the whole ten kilos, which rather shook him. He said he wouldn't have enough money for it all until a steamer came in from Corsica where he'd sent some stuff to be sold. I was just going when he told me to wait and he'd try to borrow the money from the café opposite. While he was still inside the café another man came out and said he was the grocer's brother-in-law, and that the grocer had told him to come and collect the coffee as he'd managed to borrow the money. So I brought him to the car."

"That was the man I saw?"

"Yes."

"Did he say anything else?"

"Not much. On the way down to the car he told me he'd been in the Free French Navy in England and that he was now in the police."

"What would a policeman be doing dealing in black market coffee?"

"I don't know, but he actually stopped a couple of gendarmes in the street, slapped them on the back and shook them by the hand."

"How did they react?"

"They seemed surprised."

"Probably never seen him before in their lives. What happened after that?"

"Well, when we got there you'd gone."

"Yes I know. I thought perhaps we'd arranged to meet at the Casino."

"I think he thought I was doublecrossing him and there wasn't any coffee. Anyway you soon came back and as you know we gave him the tins."

"Did he tell you anything else?"

"We didn't talk on the way back. He had a tin under each arm and walked so fast I could hardly keep up with him."

"Did you go back to the shopkeeper? What I don't see is how you came to be in the estaminet."

"After we'd collected the coffee he said that his brother-in-law was not paying enough and that he could get me a thousand francs a kilo. He bought me a glass of wine and went off with the tins saying that he would be back in a few minutes."

"The oldest confidence trick in the world."

After a moment she said, "Let's go and see the shopkeeper, there might still be a chance."

"We've wasted enough time already."

"It's on our way back."

The shop was nothing more than a stall protected from the sun by a canvas awning. The grocer, a small man with long dark hair, no collar, a white apron and espadrilles, did not seem pleased to see us. I stood helplessly listening to the exchange of French.

"He says that he hasn't got a brother-in-law. He says that he came back to tell me that he couldn't borrow the money and found I'd gone."

"You mean he didn't send the other chap over?"

"Apparently not."

"Ask him if he saw anyone come out of the café as he was trying to borrow the money."

"I'll try, but he's a bit unco-operative." She spoke to the man but he lost his temper, shouting and throwing his arms above his head. A crowd began to gather, and I could see that we were getting nowhere.

"Come on," I said. "We're wasting our time."

"I'm sorry," she said. "I shouldn't have been so greedy."

And walking back along the narrow alley I knew that she was waiting for me to say it did not matter, that she was not to blame, that the coffee was nothing. But although this was true I could not say it. I had been frightened and this stupid anger was all that remained of fear.

We found George flushed and bright-eyed. The combination of height and heat during the day had caused a resurgence of some obscure fever. He complained of pains in the stomach and wanted nothing so much as to make camp immediately.

"I'm afraid it means climbing again," I said. "It'll be impossible to find anywhere on the coast to camp. Our best plan is to get up on the Grande Corniche and find a place up there."

"Do we have to climb again? I'd rather stay down here by the sea."

"It's all built up down here. Trams run along the road by the sea, and the Moyenne Corniche is cluttered up with villas. We have to take one of the three, and although it's about fifteen hundred feet up to the top one I think it's the safest bet for a quiet camp."

"OK, let's go."

We stopped at the first flat piece of ground, a stony path running across a rocky outcrop at the highest point of the Grande Corniche. The light began to fail as we unloaded the cars. We had parked them face to face about thirty feet apart, each one astride the narrow path. I could not drive the pegs into the hard ground, so lashed the tents to the front of the cars, anchoring the sides with pieces of rock. While I struggled and cursed at the flapping canvas, Lucille came over for aspirins. "We passed an English hospital on the way up," she said. "If he's not better in the morning I'll run him down there. It's been coming on gradually all day."

Down below on the edge of the sea the Riviera was a blaze of lights, but where we were it was dark and the wind was keen and heady with the smell of pines.

We ate supper in the light of the headlamps; boiled eggs, cheese, lettuce and wine. As Sibyl finished each egg she drove the spoon through the bottom of the shell "to let the witches out," and I loved her. "There's one thing," I said, "we don't have to lug those tins around with us any more."

CHAPTER SIX

I PULLED on my shorts and espadrilles, and walked across the white road to the low stone wall which separated it from the cliffs, feeling the roughness of the rope soles under my feet. The sharp stone was already warm to my hands as I leaned over the wall to look at the sea. There were pines growing from the face of the cliff and through their blue-green needles I saw a conical hill topped by a squat rose-coloured castle. Round its crumbling walls white houses clustered, their red roofs descending the hill in crooked tiers. Below the houses the slopes were cut into terraces, white bands of gleaming limestone supporting silver-headed olives. A pale gold winding track followed the contours down into the valley, and the sun, still low in the sky, threw the whole scene into sharp relief, making the hill and the castle stand out clearly against the vigorous blue of the sea. On the far side of the bay was a low promontory gleaming in the sun and inland, in the distance, I could see the mauve misty outline of the mountains.

To my right but hidden by the cliff lay Nice, sprawling like a giant scab along the coast, its centre a concentration of tall tenements, its edges fading out into a rash of villas and small-holdings. It would already be hot down there. Somewhere, in the old crowded part of the town, was the man who had stolen our coffee beans. Were the beans still in their English biscuit tins with the tattered Huntley & Palmer labels, the lids carefully sealed with gummed paper? Or had they already been sold to one of the stucco-fronted hotels on the Promenade? I didn't blame him in the least. We had tried a tentative sortie into the black market and had come up against a professional. It had been pretty quick thinking when you come to consider it—to hear the shopkeeper come in to borrow money, appraise the situation, and walk across and introduce yourself as the man's brother-in-law. He almost deserved the coffee. Or was the shopkeeper in the know? That would explain his agitation at seeing Sibyl again. Whichever it was they had moved pretty quickly. I had seen the thief only momentarily with his linen cap, the tin of coffee beans under each arm, his absurd tight-bummed trousers. He said he'd been in the Free French Navy. Probably just a line to gain her confidence. Probably been in Nice the whole of the war, never done a day's work in his life.

After breakfast we descended to Menton and George decided that he would have his dynamo repaired. He said that he would risk one day's journey into Italy with us and would leave for home the following morning. Wanting to swim, we arranged to meet them later at the control post on the border.

Once away from the centre of the town I drove in my shorts only, enjoying the coolness of the soft air on my arms and shoulders. We had gone less than a mile when Sibyl announced that her straw hat had blown from the back of the car. We retraced our route, but there was no sign of it. In the main street of shops and cafés, I stayed in the car while she went to ask in one of the shops if anyone had noticed a straw hat. Presently she was back, excited. "I say, that man is walking down the street!"

"What man?"

"The man who stole the coffee."

I scrambled out of the car and went with her to where the man was leaning against the wall of a café, in the shade. I could tell from his relaxed sagging attitude that he was drunk. "*Monsieur!*" I said. "*Où est mon café?*"

He gazed at me, uncomprehending.

"*Le café, monsieur!*" I held him by the arm, above the rolled shirtsleeve, feeling the muscle under the thin cotton. "What have you done with our coffee?" I said it in English.

He shook off my hand, turned, and stumbled into the café.

I looked at Sibyl. "He's drunk."

"He looks more ill than drunk."

We followed him, through the bead curtain hanging in the doorway, and saw him sitting at a table. His head was buried in his arms. A woman and a girl stood behind the zinc-covered bar. I crossed the floor, sat down opposite him at the small metal table and tapped him on his naked forearm. "*Monsieur, le café.*"

"*Pas café,*" the man muttered. "*De l'eau!*"

The girl brought a glass of water. He took a large capsule

from an orange packet, put it in his mouth and swallowed the water. Although his arms were browned by the sun his face was white and moist. He buried his head in his arms again.

"*Le paludisme*," the girl said. She stood back, watching him.

"What's that?" I asked Sibyl.

"Malaria."

I felt sure that it was a conspiracy, that the girl was in league with the man. I shook him roughly by the shoulder, and this time he looked up, with a flat baleful stare. His light brown eyes showed nothing of guilt or recognition—nothing.

"Monsieur!" Sibyl spoke for the first time.

He looked at her. For a moment his eyes had depth, and comprehension. It was as though the shutter over a camera lens had lifted. Then, in a flash, they were blank and flat again. He re-buried his head in his arms.

"He recognised me—I know it's the same man."

I was certain of it, but I didn't know what to do next. I felt embarrassed sitting there in the café without my shirt. If I went back to the car to get it the man would be gone when I returned. I tapped him on the arm again, harder.

When he looked up this time there was a warning in his face. "Take care, monsieur." He spoke in English.

"The coffee. I want the money for the coffee."

He looked at me out of those blank shallow eyes. "I have no coffee."

"The coffee you took from my wife. You owe me ten thousand francs."

He made a gesture of impatience, rose to his feet and lurched out of the café. We joined him on the pavement and walked one on each side of him down the street.

"You go and look after the car," I told Sybil.

"No, I'm coming with you."

I caught the man by the arm and brought him to a standstill. He was recovered now, although his face was streaming with sweat. "Take care, monsieur!" The warning held more menace now, and I thought of the fighting tricks of the slums of Nice, the kick in the groin, the knife.

But I was committed, I couldn't back down. I was the bigger man and I made the most of this, forcing him back against the wall. "Ten thousand francs, monsieur!" I felt, as I said it, like the character in a bad film—but I knew at the same time that this was real.

"I do not know you," the man said. "What is all this talk of coffee?"

"We'll go to the gendarmerie." Somehow my threat had a familiar ring.

"*D'accord!* That will settle the matter."

Once more we began to walk, and I wondered where the gendarmerie was and what I would say when we got there. I still held the man by the arm as though I were confident the police would take my part, but I was wishing I'd never started it. Fortunately it was siesta time and no one was about.

After a few paces the man stopped. "*Alors, monsieur.* I will fetch you the money." The capitulation was sudden and came, like Tatiane's, at the very moment when he seemed to me to be winning. "I will get it from my wife who is resting with the children by the sea. If you will wait here I will come back."

I looked at him, amazed that he should try this trick again. "I'm coming with you."

He hesitated, then began to move forward. I fell into step with him, on the kerb side, wondering what the next move would be. Sibyl was on his other side, slightly behind.

A motor truck pulled up at the kerb, the driver shouting something in the *niçois* dialect. I thought he must be asking the way, and when our man crossed in front of me and stood with one foot on the running-board of the lorry I was not suspicious. There was a quick exchange which I could not understand. I stood there waiting for the conversation to finish, idly noting the shabby leather wallet which protruded from the hip pocket of the tight low-cut trousers, impatient for the lorry to move away.

When the driver suddenly let in the clutch and the lorry moved off with the man on the running-board, I was taken by surprise. Acting without thought, wishing to retain something if not the man himself, I snatched the wallet.

With a roar of unsilenced exhaust the truck rattled down the street. I saw the man clap his hand to his pocket, hesitate as though to jump, think better of it, and vanish round a turn in the road.

We stood on the pavement and searched through my prize. I had hoped that there would be enough money in it to pay for the coffee, but I was disappointed. In fact it was not a wallet at all but a small book in leatherette case, entitled *Livret de Mariage* and made out in the name of François Morino. It was rather like the forged *Ausweis* I had used in Germany. "At least we know his address," I said.

"Let's go back and call on him."

"No, we'll write the gentleman a letter."

"Why not go back to Nice? It's not far and we've got plenty of time."

"And get a knife in our ribs. No, we'll play this one from a distance. Let's go and have that swim."

Refreshed by the swim in the cool sea we lay stretched out on the soft shingle and I dictated the letter for Sibyl to translate:

Dear monsieur, Before you made your somewhat hasty departure this morning I was able to possess myself of your Livret de Mariage and am thus able to write to you. The market value of the goods that you borrowed from my wife in the café in Nice is 10,000 francs, and as no doubt the goods themselves are by now beyond your reach I shall be satisfied if you will remit that sum of money to me, poste restante, at L'Ufficio Postale, Rome, where we shall call for it three days from now.

"Three days is a bit soon," said the compleat secretary. "It's scarcely an exchange of post. Why not make it Naples?"

"Right, make it Naples. And five days. We'll post this now and send him one or two reminders on the way."

We found the frontier post between France and Italy in a state of uproar. The centre of the disturbance was a tousle-headed young man wearing a lobster-red fisherman's smock over pale green linen trousers. He was the owner of a large scarlet open Delage with English registration plates, and he seemed to be objecting to some course of action proposed by the French officials. Three gendarmes, quite as vociferous if not so loud, were standing guard over the car, while its passenger was apparently oblivious to the slanging match which was taking place above her sleek blonde head.

"What a lily." George had drawn up alongside.

"Hush!" Lucille said. "They're English."

I wished I could put on a show like that. "What's it all about?"

"It's well past the factual stage," Sibyl said. "He's dealing with their probable ancestry. He doesn't rate it very high. There's something about a ciné camera. Now he's asking them if they think he's a German spy."

When the douaniers had been routed and the scarlet car driven off into France with a screech of tyres, our less exotic English caravan was allowed to cross into Italy without being searched. The officials seemed to have lost all interest.

On the far side of the Italian barrier I waited for George. Below us the sea shimmered cool and deep and blue. "Let's find a quiet beach," I said.

"Nothing I'd like better. I want to try these out." He brandished a rubber face mask with a plate-glass visor, and a bent celluloid breathing tube with a rubber mouthpiece.

Beyond Ventimiglia the beach was deserted. After the swim I lay on the hot sand watching the back of George's head and the queer curved breathing tube with its caged ping-pong ball move purposefully about the surface of the sea. Occasionally he would surface with a splutter to empty his breathing tube of water, then he would disappear again with a splash and a flourish of legs.

I turned over on my back, every pore of my skin responding to the penetrating warmth of the sun.

"Do you know who that man at the border was?" Lucille said. "The one who was doing all the shouting?"

"No, who was it?" Sibyl asked lazily.

"I admired his guts," I said, from within my contentment, "he had a way with him, you must admit that."

"It was a famous English film director." Lucille sat up and fluffed her hair to dry in the sun. "It's been tormenting me ever since we crossed the border. I can't remember his name. You must know the one I mean, Bill."

I didn't, nor did I care very much. "What company does he make films for?"

"I don't know, but he's made a lot of important ones." She anticipated me, "I can't think of any of their names at the moment, but you must know who I mean."

"I don't—not even with my vast knowledge of the film business." All three months of it, I thought.

"What are they really like?" she said. "Are they really fantastic? Could you fix it for me to visit a studio?"

"I probably could, if there's any studio work to be done when we get back. I've never been inside one myself."

"I wish you would. What are they like, the actors? Are they very glamorous?"

"The ones we've met aren't very glamorous," Sibyl said.

"They work damned hard." I thought of what the director had said. 'I'd love making films if it weren't for the actors. If only we could do without 'em and get down to it.' Walt Disney could, of course, but he's a genius; others have to work with human beings. You can write what you like in the script, but you can't make it come out like that. "They made me work pretty hard," I said.

"Doing what?"

"Writing the script."

"Surely that's not very difficult. After all, you wrote the book." She said it as though she didn't really believe I had.

"It's not quite the same," I said. "In a book you can make a character think. You can't do that in a film."

"Are they so very dim?" Lucille sounded as though her world was falling to pieces.

I laughed. "I don't mean the actors. I mean in a book you can *say* what a character's thinking about. In a film it has to be revealed by action or dialogue." I thought of the long arguments over the dialogue during the script conferences, arguments which would get bogged down in a wrangle over a single word. A wrangle that we had taken seriously, obstinately, because we realised that this single word, whatever it was, indicated that we did not see eye to eye. It had seemed ridiculous at times, three grown men and a woman arguing over a single word, but we had been serious about it because we wanted to make a worthwhile film.

"But isn't it all terribly exciting?" Lucille said. "You'll be able to go to the première."

That's the last thing, I thought. But it was exciting. Even now I could hardly believe in that Sunday morning when we had awakened and I had picked up the three newspapers from where they had been pushed under the door of the small flat. We had read the reviews and I, leaving Sibyl in bed, had dressed hurriedly and dashed down to the paper seller on the corner of the street. I'd bought one of every paper the man had, and eleven of them had carried a review. We'd sat in bed and read them one after another, strewing them on the floor, hardly believing that it could possibly be true. That morning had wiped out every rejection slip which had accompanied the manuscript on its return from publisher after publisher over the last four years. Each time, feeling that the publisher was probably right, I'd gone through the whole book before sending it out to someone else. Sibyl had sat up typing far into the night, re-typing, discussing, encouraging; all with the same calm conviction that sooner or later we would find a publisher. But after it had come back from one of the big literary agents with a note to say that there was no market for war stories I'd put the manuscript on one side and I'd concentrated on my job of buying books instead of writing one. I answered Lucille. "It is very exciting. You don't realise how little you know about your own book until you try to make a film of it."

"I mean all the parties and everything. I'd love to go to one of Foyle's Literary Luncheons. . . ."

It was when I'd been lunching with Collins's publicity manager that he'd asked me about my escape from Germany. Instead of telling him the story I'd sent him the manuscript, although they'd turned it down once already; and this time it was not rejected. But war books were still not popular, and no one but the publicity manager had thought much of its chances. The publisher had been as surprised as I had been when it sold out on publication day.

"I think you're very lucky, Sibyl, and I don't think you appreciate it. I don't suppose you've even bought a new evening dress."

"I haven't." Sibyl flung out an arm on the hot sand, and turned her face to the sun.

"Now don't tell me that you shun publicity, because I won't believe it."

"We're very glad to have it," I told her, "so long as it sells the book." I'd been guest of honour at literary luncheons and dinners, spoken on the radio and presented prizes at schools—and my stammer had made it all a terrifying and difficult business. I could still feel the panic that had gripped me when I first faced a microphone. I'd have given almost anything to be out of it, away, outside, not having all those eyes, all those ears, all those inquiring minds waiting for me to get to my feet. It had to be done. I'd forced myself, fought down the panic, but I could feel the perspiration stand out on my skin now, half a thousand miles away. It had been harder than writing the book, much harder than making the escape.

"Take what you will, saith the Lord, but pay for it," Sibyl said.

"I think you're very cynical, both of you. If I were you,

Sibyl, I'd make him go. It's only fair." She turned to me. "Don't you like being guest of honour and making speeches?"

"It terrifies me." I saw George swimming inshore, and went down to the edge of the sea to meet him.

He pulled off his goggles. "Have a go, Bill. It's a different world down there."

I fitted the goggles over my eyes and bit firmly on the rubber mouthpiece. Here indeed was another world, beautiful and silent, pulled one way and another by the currents, calm but always moving. It was like flying. The bright fish flashing in shoals silently and swiftly across three dimensions were like other aircraft passing across your gunsights. In the shallows the waving fronds, the sandy bottom, the rocks, the fish were brilliantly coloured by the light that filtered through the clear water. Deeper it was blue and green, with dark shadows between masses of rock, and pale grey or black fish which glided smoothly between the shadows.

Here was reality. To hunt swiftly down the clear water, to feel its pull on my skin, its tug at my hair. To feel the warm sun on my shoulders as I surfaced and the cold creep in my blood as I dived below an overhanging rock. Lewis's, last year's figures, the fictitious but pandered-to 'average buyer', even the film company, faded from my mind.

It was after five by Italian time when we left the beach and in the town the people were sitting on wooden chairs on the pavement outside their houses. There were crowds of bright-eyed children playing marbles on the streets and tall straight-limbed high-breasted girls paraded gracefully in low-heeled leather sandals. As usual I had promised George we would camp early but this evening the promise was even more difficult to keep. We had not seen a suitable camping place since coming down into Menton that morning, and the road beyond Ventimiglia ran through country every square inch of which was either cultivated or unapproachable by car. We followed the coast through Bordighera and Ospedaletti, past patches of market garden in which roses and carnations grew. Small dark children stepped out in front of the cars, keeping one foot on the grass verge for safety but thrusting themselves out as far as possible and offering bunches of carnations which glowed red and pink and white in their dusky fists.

It was growing dark when we turned off to the left to strike inland away from the thickly populated coast. The main road here formed a cornice below what I thought was the top of the cliff. The descent to the beach on our right was about a hundred feet and I supposed that an equally short climb would bring us to the top, where my imagination had provided rolling fields and sheltering pines.

The track climbed gradually at first, steepening suddenly and following a series of hairpin bends that were so sharp that we had to reverse several times to get round them. The surface was loose gravel and there was nothing between us and a sheer drop to the road below. The track was so narrow that I wondered what would happen if we were to meet someone coming down. We climbed steadily for a mile and a half, with hairpin bends at hundred-yard intervals. Coming to a slightly wider stretch I stopped, put large stones under the wheels and waited for George to draw up behind.

"I say, it's a bit steep, isn't it?"

I put stones behind his wheels. "Sorry, George, I didn't think it would be so far up."

"We don't seem to be there yet."

"We'll have to go on," I said. "We can't turn round here."

George lit a cigarette and I remembered with shame his hatred of heights. From where we stood we looked down on the road below, down what seemed to be a long flight of wide steps, each step a narrow strip of land not more than a few feet wide on which wheat and sometimes grass was growing. Each terrace was revetted with rock and clods of earth and on each stood a tall cylindrical water tank. There was a tank at each bend of the track, and the whole hillside was thrown up in sharp geometrical relief of dots and lines by the evening sun.

We resumed our climb in the fading light. At every turn we expected to reach the top but the road continued up in regular inexorable zigzags. When we did gain the edge of the cliff we found olive groves, still terraced, the trees grey and hoary; and we followed the narrow road into a village of dark stone with slitted walls built on the lip of the sheer mountainside. The single street led straight to the square, bounded on one side by the town hall and on the others by tall houses with slatted shutters, shrouded by the rapidly falling night. Dark Moorish faces peered from the greater darkness of the doorways. Children had been playing in the dust, but on the arrival of the strangers they stopped their game and watched; not shyly, but with a hostility that barred them from the usual clamorous demand for gum.

In the silence I got down from the car and looked at George, who shrugged his shoulders in defeat. The road ended here, in the square, and there was nothing for it but to turn and go back.

The drive down the winding track was worse than the climb. It was dark now and George was doubtful of his brakes. I drove slowly in front of him to act as a buffer should they fail. Stones loosened by his wheels overtook us in the darkness, tumbled over the edge and crashed through the trees below. Bats attracted by the lights dived and zoomed like fighters attacking a heavy bomber. Sibyl had heard that once a bat has fastened itself in your hair it will not let go and the only way to release it is to cut away the hair. I tried to reassure her but she covered her head with a scarf, and we continued down, sliding dangerously round the bends and waiting on each straight for George to come up with us.

Back on the coast road I accosted a cyclist in a puce-coloured sports shirt with an Italian sentence which I read haltingly from the phrasebook. "Excuse me, sir, is there a camping ground hereabouts?" But the man did not understand and George, who had recovered, came to the rescue by miming the erection of a tent in the light of the headlamps. A wild-eyed giant wearing white shorts and a khaki bush-jacket, he mouthed Italian words interlarded with French and Arabic and hammered non-existent tent pegs into the hard road. The man mounted his bicycle and pedalled off as fast as he could go.

We stopped outside the station of San Remo to ask again. As soon as the cars came to a standstill we were boarded by a gang of touts in peaked porter's caps who shouted the name of their patron hotel and tried to stand on the running-board to escort their salvage into harbour. I pushed them off right and left shouting, "*Accampamento, accampamento!*" but they could not or would not understand and pressed closer breathing garlic and sour wine. Behind, there was a similar scrimmage round the other car and above the gabble of Italian I could hear George shouting, "*Imshi, yallah!*" and its equivalent in English. I let in the clutch and lurched forward, scattering those who were in front and dropping the others one by one as I accelerated.

It was near midnight when we asked the advice of a group of men who were standing under a lamp outside a brickworks. This time it was Sibyl who tried the phrasebook question, and they understood her. It seemed to me as I waited, the men discussing it eagerly, a foolish request late at night on the outskirts of a town, to ask where there was open country where we could camp; but we were lucky. One of the men knew just the place, the garden of a deserted villa owned by a lady from Texas who had not been here since the war. The villa had been occupied first by the Germans and then by the Allies, and now the local people used the garden to grow vegetables.

We put up the tents on an overgrown path under palm trees at the edge of a patch of artichokes. I was tired and hungry and when I found that the cork had come out of the bottle of wine in the back of the car I could not face unloading and cleaning up the mess that night. I rigged a small lamp on a flex from the car to provide light for Sybil's cooking and, slowly, I became aware that we were not alone. Above the incessant whirring of the cicadas and the croaking of the frogs there was an indistinct murmur of voices. We were surrounded by a ring of pale brown expressionless faces, a ring that expanded slightly when I moved but tightened when I was still, imperceptibly closing in until, glancing up suddenly, I looked full into the face of a youth who backed quickly. I felt like the trapper in Jack London's story, encircled by the wolves which crept nearer and nearer as the fire died down.

CHAPTER SEVEN

In two columns, one up and one down, the ants had been routed via one of the wire spokes to the hub, along the spring, out underneath the running-board, up the sticky path of dried wine which had trickled down the slippery side of the car and in through the door which I had left ajar. They were scattered over the floor, busily crawling round and filling their stomachs with wine, then joining the returning column to their nest where I knew they would share it out among themselves by regurgitation, face to face, stroking one another's antennæ as a signal to disgorge.

I crouched on the dusty path in the already warm morning sun, fascinated by their organisation. How had the sexless discoverer of this store of food informed its fellow workers? Who had decided not to eat the dried wine which formed the path up the vertical surface of the car, that there was more to be gained by leaving this easily accessible booty? Would they finally withdraw down this path, eating it as they went?

In Germany I had kept an ant-lion, a revolting object I called Hermann, dark grey with a hairy belly and wicked claws, in a tin of sand on the shelf above my bunk. I used to watch him dig his cone-shaped pit by walking doggedly backwards in decreasing circles, ploughing up the sand and throwing it clear with flicks of his head. When the sides were sloping smoothly to his satisfaction he would bury himself in the bottom of the cone, and wait. Sooner or later an ant, or some other insect, would cross the lip of the crater and start to slide. If he showed any sign of getting out again Hermann would fling sand at him with savage flicks of his spade-like head until the victim rolled within reach of those wicked claws. And when Hermann had sucked his meal he would toss the husk out of the pit and wait for more. Revolting as he was, he personified patience, a virtue I had need of at the time. Later he had turned into a dragonfly and flown out over the wire. I had looked him up in the camp library, and had become interested in ants.

Nothing could have been more depressing to a prisoner in a cage than a study of the ant. These insects had been living a community life for millions of years, were keeping cattle and growing crops in underground chambers when we humans were still grubbing about for beetles under stones. The evolution of the ant had brought him to such a pitch that the individual had ceased to exist. Mass mind had taken the place of individual thinking so that one single instinct, or intelligence, could direct this army to my car and instruct them to leave the trickle of dried wine as a path for others to follow.

The more I, behind my wire, learned of the ant, who cannot eat except by taking food from another ant's stomach, the more we seemed to follow in his footsteps. An ant, alone, can die of hunger surrounded by food. The modern human, who receives his emotions of joy, sorrow, pity and contempt predigested from the radio or the television screen, can remain as stone surrounded by the real joys and sorrows of the world. I thought of men I knew, roused to a pitch of emotional pity for the under-privileged races, people they had never seen, whose way of life was unknown to them. Not that they themselves would do anything to help. They would weep their facile crocodile tears and at the same time would act as sadists to their wives. To live vicariously had become more pleasant than to cope with life; to suffer and to pity by the thousand easier than to act alone.

If the death of a single ant seemed necessary for the convenience of the mass, that ant committed suicide. It was not that the individual recognised the need and made the sacrifice. The mass mind thought for all. And it seemed to me that we were heading that way. Very soon we should believe only what we were told on the radio, and work blindly for the good of mankind not knowing that there was ever such a thing as individual man. That, I thought, is why war is so dangerous for the community, it encourages people to think and adventure for themselves—especially if they are kept behind barbed wire with nothing else to do. I remained depressed until I realised that it is only by our individual intelligence that we are aware of the freedom that we might be losing—that we still have time.

We were driving on into Italy along a new corniche road which tunnelled now through the golden rock, now through groves of lemon trees on which the pale-green fruit hung luminously among the darker leaves. Then we would burst out into warm sunshine high above the sea on which brightly painted toy boats with coloured sails spread their pale-blue nets.

It was strange to have no car behind us, and I thought of George and Lucille on their way back to the flat in Dolphin Square; of the office where George would find his secretary waiting, his business lunches, meetings and committees. George would be dealing in thousands of pounds, taking a chance on the market, gambling, making decisions. But none of the money would be his, all of it was one step removed from reality.

It's the same with you, I told myself. If you gamble on a book, buy huge quantities of a novel in the belief that it will be a success, and it flops and has to be sold off cheaply later, the loss isn't yours. If you finish the year a few thousands short of profit you're unpopular, but again the loss is not yours. There's the possibility of being sacked of course, but that's unlikely.

And it is exciting in a way, it has its moments. You sit there on a Monday morning behind your desk in the London office, and in succession the representatives of the various publishing houses come in with their new books. You know the 'reps' pretty well by now, who's telling you the truth and who's shooting a line. You know which publishers will keep their promise to back with national publicity the 'big book of the year' and which, once they have safely unloaded it on to you, will forget all about it and be busy trying to sell another 'biggest-ever seller' before the ink is dry on the last. It's exciting to sit there spending money among the publishers, even if it isn't your money, knowing that you're backing your own judgment and that you have to accept everything that's said as sales talk, no matter how friendly you become. I'd once heard a sales director talking on the telephone to another buyer: 'Yes old boy, no old boy, yes—we'll change the cover with the next impression. I'm sorry you think it's indecent old boy.' I'd seen him put down the telephone, turn to his secretary and say, 'The interfering bastard.' That had been in the early days, soon after the war, before I'd learned to accept it as a matter of course. Later there had been the literary party where the best-selling author, just a little drunk, had taken me to one side and said solemnly, 'Never trust a publisher. They're twisters, every bloody one of them—and mine's the biggest twister of the lot.'

I'd taken the job over with only a few months' training. It was a policy of Lewis's that if you were efficient at one thing you could be equally efficient at another, and they'd think nothing of paying a barrister a handsome salary to manage a hardware department. In the same way they would cheerfully change him over from hardware to haberdashery; and he would have to sink or swim. Most of us managed to keep afloat. They must have been right, because the number of brigadiers and DSOs who came back after the war was staggering.

Those first few months buying the stock for the book departments in seven large retail stores had been hectic. I had thought I knew as much about contemporary literature as the next man, but the trouble was that the best-selling titles were written by people whose names I had never heard, particularly in the lending library. So I began by asking the publisher's representative what he really thought of the chances of the book he was trying to sell, and if he lied to me I never believed him again. I missed a few best-sellers in that way, but on the whole it worked. After a time I began to think that I could anticipate the public taste and to fancy that I could tell by the feel of a book in my hand whether I could sell it in any quantity. And how often I was wrong. . . .

By now the corniche road was crowded with motorists from Genoa and by cyclists who pedalled easily up slopes that would bring most Englishmen to their feet. Even girls, their cotton skirts flowing gracefully round their brown legs, cycled unswervingly up the steepest hills.

Sometimes we left the coast for a short distance but always returned, to catch sudden glimpses of blue sea, crowded sandy beaches and small fishing villages. In one we saw the half-built skeleton of a boat bigger than the largest house, with curved prow like an ancient galley, standing on its stocks, its white planed ribs gleaming in the sun. In another the high-stemmed fishing boats were pulled up on to the beach where they rested clumsily on their sides like stranded fish, and light brown nets were hung to dry on wooden racks. In the cafés on the waterfront and walking along the streets were young girls in white confirmation frocks and small boys with plastered hair and clean white shirts, escorted by their parents in dull and Sunday black. And everywhere the sun blazed back from colour-washed houses and white streets, flashing and rippling off the silver olive trees and darting with sparks of fire from the brilliant blue of the sea.

Savona had been badly bombed and little seemed to have been done to repair the damage. Here again we saw the blocks of houses sheared as though by a knife, with beds still standing on half floors, rows of mantelpieces on outer walls, and flights of stairs that stopped suddenly in broken jagged concrete. The damage here was emphasised by the ragged linen draped over balcony railings and by the roads which, at their best, had been paved with huge flagstones and were now uneven and broken by the bombing. Double trams like clockwork trains clattered along the cobbled streets and outside the station stood ancient landaus with starved decrepit horses sleeping in the sun. In the main street the sun was hidden by tall houses connected by archways, and everywhere there was dust from the ruined buildings.

We skirted the docks, where wartime minesweepers and corvettes rubbed sides with fishing boats amid a desolation of crumbled stone and twisted metal, and on the outskirts of the town ran into another bicycle race. This one must have been nearing its end, for the cyclists had almost reached the limit of their endurance and were pedalling their spidery machines listlessly through the cheering crowds. Some of the competitors wore crash helmets with goggles, some padded leather helmets like those worn by American footballers, others white jockey caps with exaggerated scoop-shaped peaks. A few were content with a handkerchief tied at its four corners.

We sat in the car and watched the favourite pass. He was not the leader but it was for him that the crowd gave its loudest cheer. On his face was an aloof expression, almost of dedication. Sweat had washed clean channels down his dust-grimed cheeks and there were white circles round his eyes although the goggles that had left the marks were now pushed up so that his fans could see his face. He wore a thin black athletic vest with a spare inner tube crossed over his back, and he crouched low over the handlebars on which were clipped two aluminium flasks of liquid food. His brown hairy thighs bunched under their thin covering of cotton as he thrust his way through the gaping crowds. After the teams had passed the crowds closed in, jabbering excitedly, jostling in the heat of the sun for a last look at their sweat-stained, mud-bespattered hero.

Personally I would not cross the road to watch a football match. There is a void in me where most people keep a flame of loyalty to a particular team or player. Such newspaper headlines as WOLVES FIGHT IT OUT WITH SPURS or TIGERS TEAR INTO HUDDERSFIELD do not fill me with enthusiasm or alarm. As a boy I enjoyed playing games but even then the joy was in the burning of cold air in overworked lungs, the bringing of every effort to push the ball across the line or confound my opponent with a tricky shot.

I was still playing rugger when I joined Lewis's and in one match I was knocked out, to wake up hours later, concussed, in a private ward of the village hospital. I had only ten pounds in the world and I knew that I could not pay the bill. It was after dark and the electric light was on. I found my clothes in a cupboard and began to get dressed, but a nurse came in and tried to get me back to bed. I had some crazy idea about not staying if I could not pay the bill, and she had to fetch the Matron, who gave me something to keep me quiet. I worried until George came to see me and said that the firm would pay for everything. I have never forgotten how relieved I felt to hear it. Now George had turned for home and I was driving on to make a film instead of going back with him, and I felt ridiculously alone and unprotected.

The sky clouded over and it began to rain. We raised the hood and ate lunch in the car while the rain dripped dismally from the pines and the sea, which had been white and blue and gold with patches of red, turned uniformly grey.

"We'd better write another note to Morino," I said.

"What, already?"

"We mustn't give him time to relax. We'll post it in Genoa as we go through."

Monsieur [we wrote], *I would remind you that I expect to find the ten thousand francs you owe me awaiting my arrival at the post office in Naples. Should the money not be there I intend to request the British Consul to report the whole affair to the Chief of Police in Nice, to your undoubted disadvantage. Believe me, monsieur, I mean what I say.*

"There's an empty threat if ever there was one," Sibyl said.

It had stopped raining when we drove into the city but the sky was still grey and the uneven cobblestones were coated with slippery mud. Genoa had been even more badly bombed than Savona and was far bigger, so that we had more time in which to notice the destruction.

I had contributed to this destruction. Four times I had swayed in the air above Genoa, sick with fear, my eye to the bombsight, watching the increasingly lovely crimson roses and wreaths of fire glittering and scintillating thousands of feet below. Four times I had given my slow instructions to the pilot as the fires slid erratically along the wires of the bomb-sight. Four times I had pressed the bomb-switch and felt the aircraft lift as the bombs fell, felt myself pressed hard against the floor of the fuselage and then lifted inches into the air, as the pilot banked and jinked the aircraft out of the search-light beams. And now, driving through this battered town seven years after I had dropped the bombs, I wanted to apologise.

At the entrance to the docks we were stopped by a crowd of dark, desperate characters, dissipated starlings in cloth caps and scraps of GI uniform. They flourished jerricans of petrol and, when I asked the price, quoted three times as much as we had paid in France. I declined the offer and drove on again, glad to leave the town behind, not stopping to inspect the cemetery about which our postman at home in England had enthused. A naval pensioner, he had visited Genoa with the Fleet before the war, and to him its shining jewel had been the cemetery. 'A lovely cemetery, all stone angels and images of dead people, just like life. All done in marble. I used to go up there of a Sunday afternoon. . . . Dunno what it's like now, of course, now that the Americans have had it.'

I had often wondered what he feared the Americans had done.

I brought the car to rest in the only parking space, next to an enormous open Packard with white-painted tyres. I had hardly pulled on the handbrake before my door was wrenched open by an attendant who obviously expected to be rewarded for this unnecessary service. The fact that he had opened my door and not Sibyl's I put down to the possibility that he had so often been bilked by the driver walking off without paying—which is exactly what I did.

At first sight Portofino had appeared to be merely a fishing village, with its small cobbled square leading down to the calm sea, its few shops and cafés with tables set out in front of them. Then we saw that the café tables were spread with white cloths and lavishly shaded by fringed umbrellas, that the shop windows were full of expensively simple clothes, hand-made lace and elaborate equipment for underwater fishing, that on the water floated clean, white and luxurious yachts. Critical eyes stared from behind dark glasses as we walked to the water's edge and looked at the boats. The road ended here, there was no way round the headland. From the quayside the land rose to the mountains, the lower slopes dotted with opulent villas set far apart among the trees.

"We can't camp here," Sibyl said.

"We'll find somewhere." I felt we had made a mistake in coming to this exclusive stretch of coast. "We'll drive back the way we came. But first we'll get those goggles and a harpoon gun. There's no point in swimming without them once you've seen what's down there."

I pulled off the road on to a small rocky promontory jutting out into the sea and we sat there for some minutes enjoying the quiet of the evening. It might have been a hundred miles from the urbanity of Portofino. Slowly, mirrored on the still water, a small boat with red sails crossed the mouth of the cove.

"What about a swim?" I wanted to show her the new world I had discovered.

"We ought to find somewhere to camp." She turned and looked at the steep cliff above the road. A few yards up, approached by a narrow winding path, was a ruined cottage with a garden beside it. The cottage was almost hidden by an enormous fig tree. "What about pitching up there?"

"It's a devil of a way to lug the tent. We'd never get the car up."

"We can leave the car here, and trust to luck. When we've put the tent up we'll have that swim."

I stood knee-deep on the rocks at the sea's edge and plunged into the water. At once everything that had been blue and gold and vibrating with light was muted. Here the light struck obliquely through the mirror of the sea. Colours there were, but all subdued. Even the blue catapult gun that I held in my right hand had changed colour and glowed like an irridescent snake when I thrust it before me as I swam; and all weight had gone, so that the three-foot metal gun was as light as a wand and I lay on the buoyancy of the water as though I were on wings.

We hunted for some time along the rocks of the coast, enjoying the softly drifting movement of the underwater world. At times surging clouds of bubbles would swirl down the face of the vertical rock to remind me that a few inches above my head there was a slight chop on the surface of the sea which slapped against the encrusted rocks, but here, below the surface, all was calm and smoothly pulling.

We set up the table by the car on the edge of the sea and ate the steaks that Sibyl had bought earlier in the day. We drank Chianti and, as the moon rose in the sky, we climbed the hillside to the tent and finished the meal with figs from the neglected garden.

High on our shelf we felt removed from the world, fresh and cool and free from interference. Wc lay naked, as we always did, with the tent flaps thrown wide open and only the mosquito-net between us and the moon which glowed so warmly in the sky. From the road below came the sound of footsteps and then, pure and sad and lovely in the stillness, a clear controlled voice singing a Neapolitan fishing song.

Hearing it now, in the soft darkness of the Italian night, I remembered Stockholm in 1943 and a fair-haired girl with a halo of lighted candles on her head. Sancta Lucia, the symbol of light in the long Swedish winter. The tune was Italian, but the words and the weary wait for the sun were purely Scandinavian. December 13th was Saint Lucia's day, and I still remembered with a catch at my heart the loving kindness of that solemn child who had brought cakes and coffee and good wishes to the stranger in the morning, walking so carefully because of the lighted candles in her hair.

Suddenly, lying in the small tent under the fig tree, I was wide awake. Everything was quiet, but the quiet was alive. I lifted myself carefully, not to awaken Sibyl, and looked out under the flap of the tent. Below the rocky platform on which the car stood, held steady off the rocks by a man with a long pole, was a boat; not a fishing boat like those which still floated with their lights in a string across the bay, but a smart white motor cruiser. Looking more carefully, I saw that she was a converted MTB.

Men were moving silently about her deck. One jumped ashore and climbed swiftly up on to the promontory. Two others followed, and another figure emerged from the shadow of a pine tree on the edge of the road and joined them. The men from the boat seemed disconcerted by the sight of the car. They spoke quietly, gesticulating towards it, and the other man seemed to be excusing himself, but also quietly; so that it was for me, up there on my ledge, all in dumb show. For a few minutes they stood still by the car, but not touching it, and then they seemed to make up their minds. Quickly and silently the four of them climbed down the rock face and jumped aboard the boat. The engine started, the man pushed hard with his pole, the boat reversed slowly, turned and moved out to sea. Soon the sound of the engine was lost in the slap, slap of water against the rocks. She must have silencers, I thought.

I pulled on my trousers and climbed down to check that the car cover had not been disturbed. Everything seemed intact, but in future we must always pitch the tent beside the car.

CHAPTER EIGHT

I HAD BEEN fishing for our breakfast and was returning emptyhanded. I would have to learn to dive deeper and hold my breath longer if I was to spear any of those worthwhile fish which lurked so tantalisingly in the greater depths. Several times that morning I had sent my slim steel harpoon on its nylon thread snaking towards its quarry but always he was out of range. What fish I had encountered near the surface had been small, nervous and difficult to approach.

Swimming to the shore I could see that there was another car parked on the road beside the Bentley and as I climbed the rocks I recognised the Packard we had seen in Portofino. The driver, a man of my own age or slightly younger, was talking to Sibyl.

"No luck?" By the colour of his skin and the striped short-sleeved vest he was wearing I had taken him for an Italian, and the English accent came as a surprise. "You won't catch much without oxygen round here now."

"They're all too deep for me."

"You need a breathing outfit. I was just telling your wife, we caught a *mérou* that tipped the scales at fifty kilos off the Moroccan coast last week. But you've got to go down for 'em. It used to be quite good along this coast but it's getting fished out now I'm afraid." He took a packet of American cigarettes from his pocket and offered them to me.

"No thanks."

"Neither of you?" He said it as though I had admitted that we were both illiterate, or worse.

I put down the harpoon-gun and began to dry myself on the towel Sibyl handed me. I was hungry and wished the man would go away. "No fish for breakfast," I told her.

"We'll have eggs and bacon for a change," she said.

"Yes please, I'm hungry."

But the stranger seemed in no hurry. He sat himself on the running-board of the Bentley. "I read your book and enjoyed it very much."

Oh hell, I thought, not on an empty stomach. "It's very kind of you to say so."

"I was in the SBS myself."

"The Filibusters."

The man grinned. "That's right."

I decided that it was possible. In spite of the narrow gold chain round his neck and the somewhat colourful outfit he looked tough.

"My name's Lambert. What do you think of doing with yourself when you've made this film? Are you taking your own part in it?"

I laughed. "I'm no actor. We're just going to hang around while they shoot it."

"A bit of a swan, eh?"

"That's right."

"Then what?"

"I'm not sure."

Lambert lit another cigarette. "Please don't think I'm merely being inquisitive." Which was exactly what I was thinking, but there was no point in saying so.

"I'm going to cook breakfast," Sibyl said quickly. "Have you had yours?"

"Thank you very much, I never eat it. But if you're making coffee——"

"I am," she told him.

"What did you do after you got home?" He was a persistent sort of chap. "Join MI9 like all the rest?"

"I did for a time. . . . Then I took a pilot's course." I thought perhaps he was a journalist.

"But you can navigate."

"I could. I was a navigator until I was shot down."

"And now you're doing what?"

"I'm in the book trade."

"No, I mean as a job."

"That's what I mean. I buy books for a chain of stores in the provinces."

"My God." He waited until I was spreading the hard white Italian bread with butter and honey before he returned to the attack. "Will you be writing any more books?"

"If I can find anything to write about."

"I can make you a proposition."

"What's that?" I guessed it would be an article for a magazine, or perhaps a film script.

"If you're the man I think you are—you could do a lot worse than join us." He seemed to be taking long enough to get to the point, almost feeling his way there.

"Join you in what?"

"I'm running a Special Boat Service of my own. More or less the same sort of thing that we were doing in the war."

So that was it. The Packard fell smoothly into place. "What do you use," I said, "fishing boats or converted MTBs?"

"So you were awake last night. . . . Don't you think Mario has a superb voice? I tell him he ought to be singing at La Scala, but he prefers a more adventurous life—and a more profitable one."

"How profitable?"

"I can promise you five thousand a year. Tax free."

I looked at Sibyl, who looked away.

"Listen," Lambert said. "How much did they pay you for this film of yours?" Say ten thousand. . . ." Did he guess or know? "How much of that will you keep? You'll be lucky if you get a thousand after tax is paid. Where's next year's coming from?"

That's what I'm wondering, I thought. I looked out across the blue sea at a pink house standing on a rock. There was a white boat moored to a concrete quay at the foot of a crooked flight of steps. Four people, brown limbs and brightly coloured patches of clothing, were climbing aboard. "I'd like time to think it over. I've got to make this film."

"They'll get on all right without you—better probably."

"It's part of the contract."

Lambert lit another cigarette. "Come with me on one trip—both of you. We'll be back in a week. See for yourselves."

I felt the pressure. I knew that it wouldn't end with one trip. If we went now, we were committed. I shook my head. "I'm not your man I'm afraid."

"Pity." He got to his feet. "OK. Remember me to London when you get back." He climbed into the Packard and started the engine. "If you change your mind you'll find me around." He pressed the accelerator and moved away with a crunch of tyres.

I turned to Sibyl. "I've just thrown away a fortune."

"You really wanted to do it." She sat with her mug of coffee in both hands and looked at me across the brim.

"I do in a way. . . . I'd have given my ears for the chance when I got back from Germany. In fact Mike and I were interviewed by SOE, but they all offered us was a staff job in London. I suppose, with operational losses, this chap is getting a bit short of people he can trust, and if he can co-opt someone who isn't a professional crook but doesn't mind taking a risk, he's not so likely to be doublecrossed."

"Well, I'm willing. What would it be, cigarettes?"

"It wouldn't stop at cigarettes, that's the trouble. Soon it would be drugs, and shooting matches with the police. I've seen the inside of one prison, that's enough for me. It's one thing to smuggle a couple of guns and a few tins of coffee beans when it's your own property and you object to form-filling, but this is another matter. Did you notice how he smoked?"

"He never stopped. They were duty-free of course."

I laughed. "You're a romantic, that's your trouble. How did you get talking?"

"He just pulled up and asked if we were camping. Then he asked where you were, and where we were going—and before I knew where I was I'd told him all."

"You didn't stand a chance," I said. "Look how I unbuttoned. He was pretty smooth, I'll say that for him. But did you notice how he brought out the old one, *If you're the man I think you are . . .*? When a man says that you know he's going to pull a fast one."

"I rather liked him."

"So did I. But I don't like his set-up. I'd only be swapping one organisation for another."

"It would be wonderful experience for another book."

"Look," I said, "let's keep this thing simple. The problem is not whether I turn crooked or go straight, but whether I chuck a good job to try to live by writing."

"So smuggling's out, is it?"

"That was decided in a bistro in the slums of Nice if you remember."

She leaned forward and kissed me on the mouth. "Life's exciting as it is."

We turned down a road marked FOLLONICA, to a tawdry seaside town full of holiday chalets. The beach, like every other beach we had passed that day, was built up with cafés and lidos. The sand was only approachable through one or other of the wooden kiosks in which the tenant of that stretch of beach waited to collect his fee. I drove slowly along the front, hoping to come to the end of the houses, to the deserted beach which I felt sure was there. The houses became newer and newer, finally petering out into half-built chalets and then mere foundations of chalets and sites for sale. We were brought to a sudden halt by the ending of the road in soft sand and a single strand of barbed wire on which hung a faded sign, PRIVATA.

"That's that," I said. "Let's try the other direction."

The road running southward from the town was not so populated and we soon came to the end of the summer houses. First we tried a narrow lane which led past a farm on to the beach, but the place had been used by picnickers and was fouled with greasy paper and old tins and bottles. Farther on was an official camping site enclosed by barbed wire. The square paddock shaded by pine trees looked cool and clean, but the barbed wire was enough. We pressed on until the camping site was far behind and there was nothing but pine trees and the cool blue sea beyond. Turning on to the smooth carpet of pine needles we went right through the belt of trees to the edge of the sea, where short grass grew between the beach and the wood.

I switched off the engine, got down and stretched my arms above my head. The scent of pine mingled with the smell of the sea and the sun hot on the sand. The trees were tall and straight with bare trunks up to the spreading tops, pink in patches where the peasants had split the black outer bark for kindling. In front of us was the sea, with the island of Elba in the distance, and inland I could see the hills, pine-clad, with an occasional white box-like house and geometrical vineyard or field of golden wheat.

"Worth waiting for, wasn't it?"

"It's always worth waiting for," she said.

We had been driving all afternoon along the flat dusty coast road, with the railway between us and the sea. There was no way across, and it had been tantalising to know that a quarter of a mile beyond that steel ribbon were long sandy beaches with pine trees growing almost to the water's edge. We had taken one side lane that led to a level crossing and had sat there by the lowered barrier, hoping that the train would pass and that the gate would be raised to let us through. After some minutes a girl had come from a nearby house to say that the gate was never opened. We had tried several times to get away from the main road, towards the coast, but there was always the railway to make an impassable barrier between us and the sea. Sibyl had suggested striking inland into the hills which rose cool and inviting to our left, but I had wanted to swim. I had imagined pitching the tent on the shore with pine trees behind and the plunge 'into cleanness leaping', the muted colours and elusive fish.

Now at last, standing in the shade of the trees with the wind blowing in from the sea and the exciting smell of the sun on the living pines, I could imagine the coast of Italy as it had been in Shelley's time. I could almost believe in the cremation again. As a boy I had been fascinated by this burning of the body of a friend, as impressed as I had been by the ritualistic burning of the body of Beau Geste 'with the corpse of a dog at his feet'. I had imagined the long empty shore with dark clouds above and darker pines pressing down to the sea, the busy Trelawney and the black-cloaked figures of Byron and Hunt standing on that lonely sand as the smoke rose sluggishly from the pyre. Years afterwards the pall of black smoke from a crashed aircraft had completed my knowledge with the smell of burning flesh; and now this morning I had driven through Viareggio. The pines were there, but houses had been built among them and the long empty beach was crowded with sunbathers. The road was lined with open-air dance floors, cinemas and restaurants, and there had been a dozen or so British cars parked outside the Hotel du Londres.

Later we had come suddenly into Pisa through a stone arch across the road, and seen the Leaning Tower. My imagination had always set this on an arid plain, tall and stark with its sideways tilt emphasised by the unequivocal flatness of the countryside. To my disappointment the tower, fatter and shorter than I had expected, was built alongside the cathedral where it seemed ill at ease beside the tiled dome. But the view from the top had been worth the climb up the narrow spiral stairs which had reminded me of the tower at school. Only once unless he became a prefect with the right to carve his initials on one of its beams did a boy climb the tower, and I had only climbed it once. I can still remember its narrowness and the way it moved in the wind and my feeling of sickness as I looked down on the quadrangle. The Tower of Pisa did not move in the wind, but it had leaned so much out of the vertical that on one side the upward climber seemed to go downhill.

As I drove in the tent pegs I noticed the ant-lion pits. I dug one up to show to Sibyl, and together we watched him dig a new pit in the grey fibrous sand.

We looked up when we heard bells, not church bells with their note of warning but the thin metal bells which peasants hang round the necks of their animals and which have a friendly reassuring sound. A flock of sheep flowed round the trees, followed by a tall old man with a long staff and wearing faded blue cotton shirt and trousers and a large straw hat. He would have passed without speaking but I said "*Buon giorno!*" and he stopped, leaning on his staff. He spoke in dialect, and no understood word passed between us; yet by signs and by repeating simple words of our own language accompanied by signs it was established that the tent was much admired and that the shepherd approved of camping, and that Sibyl and I loved Italy, the sun, the pines and the sea. He drank some of our wine and, leaving us to our solitude, took his sheep farther along the beach where they foraged among the scanty grass.

A moment later a German Volkswagen came bumping through the wood. The windows were closed and both the driver and his woman passenger were wearing white cotton motoring helmets. The car stopped by the tent and the driver, in leather shorts and checked woollen shirt, came hurrying towards us, map in hand. His wife, looking hot and tired, stayed in the car.

"*Bitte, sprechen Sie deutsch?*"

"*Ein bischen,*" I said.

The German waved the map, and I took it from him and placed my finger on the spot where we were camped. "*Hier!*"

He looked round him despairingly at the trees, the sea and the hills. "Camping!" he said.

"*Hier!*" I demonstrated the wide expanse of clear ground, swinging my arm wide in an attempt to suggest that it was not essential to camp on this particular spot but that all the wood was free.

The German shook his head vigorously and pointed to a

symbol on the map which indicated an official camping site. "*Wasser!*" he said. "*Toiletten!*"

I pointed down the road towards the place we had passed. "*Funf Kilometer! Auto-Camping! Wasser! Toiletten! Viel Deutsch, viel Auto! Lager, Camping Lager!*" It was a very long speech for me in a foreign language.

The German beamed and bowed in his tight leather shorts. "*Danke schön! Auf wiedersehen!*"

We watched the Volkswagen bump eagerly back on to the road. "There's a man who knows what he wants," I said. "Give him a small patch of ground surrounded by barbed wire, stick notices up telling him just what to do and what not to do, lay on chlorinated water and a stinking hole in the ground called *Toiletten*, and he's happy. Give me the wide open spaces and a trowel."

When we went down to the sea to swim we found it dirty with long brown strings of rushes and refuse from the port. "It must be a sort of backwater," Sibyl said, "that's why it hasn't been exploited as a holiday resort. Everything gets washed up here." We looked at the wooden crates, tin cans, bottles and other rubbish that littered the edge of the sea.

"I don't think I'll swim after all," I said. "You wouldn't see a thing."

CHAPTER NINE

As I left the cool stone hall of the London Film Corporation building and stepped into the hot Roman sunshine I saw a policeman wearing white tropical drill and a solar topee standing by the car. Sibyl was in the driver's seat, and the policeman had a notebook in his hand.

"He keeps asking me for a thousand-lire fine for parking." She moved into the other seat. "I've been pretending I don't understand."

I took my cue from her and when he again demanded the levy I too pretended not to understand. I do not like summary justice; it can so easily be abused. I knew the police in France could impose fines without the sanction of the court, but I did not know whether they had this power in Italy.

The policeman thrust his notebook forward for me to see. There were some words I could not read and underneath, very clearly, the symbol for one thousand lire. I examined it admiringly, and then climbed into the car. He held out a white gloved hand, palm cupped in the international gesture. I took the hand, shook it warmly, said "*Grazie*," and drove away.

"How did it go?" she said.

"They're starting the film on time, unfortunately, so we'll have to turn north soon. I saw a chap called Peter Moore, and I asked him for the names of some publishers here in Rome, but apparently the biggest Italian publishers are Mondadori, in Milan. He offered to send them the book with a note, so I left the copy with him. He said if we called to see Mondadori on our way through Milan, they might be able to give us a decision by then."

"What about the publishers here in Rome?" She was not to be sidetracked.

"We can't very well offer it to anyone else at the same time."

"Why not?"

"Well, you don't. It's a sort of unwritten law. Supposing

you sent it to six publishers all at the same time and they all accepted it?"

"You'd take the best offer."

I laughed. "Publishers don't look at it like that."

"I don't see why. You did it with the film companies."

"You're too logical. Publishers consider that if they take the trouble to read a manuscript no one else must have an option until they've turned it down."

She thought for a moment. "We could try the Roman publishers now, and if we don't have any luck let him send it to Mondadori."

"Mondadori's the biggest publisher in Italy," I said. "Supposing it's accepted by some tin-pot chap here in Rome and Mondadori would have taken it after all? We'd be worse off."

She saw the sense of that. "All right. I want to get out into the country as much as you do."

We had driven into Rome through the reclaimed land of the Maremma, through fields of standing ripening wheat, forests of oak and patches of scrub studded with wild broom. There had been vast fields of vegetables with giant hoses like howitzers angling high jets of brown water into the air, pine forests just old enough to cast a shade, and then market gardens and a straight concrete road flanked by tall blocks of new flats. Before we were well into Rome we had longed to be out of it again.

The road out was broad and straight and full of traffic, lined by houses whose chimneys belched smoke. The cars puffed smoke from their exhaust pipes and even the people in the streets sucked smoke from paper tubes. Beyond the houses the blue sea glistened in the sun and the Bentley ran as though on rails along the hot straight track of black tar.

We had driven through Capua and the country was still impossible for camping. The market gardens seemed endless and the roads were more crowded than ever before. "We shall be in Naples before long," I said.

"Let's stop and have tea. Ten minutes' rest in the shade and then we'll start looking seriously."

I sat gratefully in the shade of a lime tree and studied the map, trying to decide which was the best road to the least inhabited stretch of country. What we needed was a map showing density of population. The lime was in full flower, and the air was heavy with the sound of honey-bees droning among the leaves.

A small caravan of gypsies came slowly down the road; a pony and trap, driven by the man, piled high with brushwood and followed by his pregnant wife on foot. A young girl walked alone some distance from the trap, and a smaller boy, scarcely old enough to walk, strayed erratically behind. The man and woman passed unheeding but the girl came across to where we sat. She crouched at my feet, held out a dirty hand and whispered something in Italian. I had no idea what she was saying but the action and the tone of voice were clear enough, as was the cringing near-certainty that she would be rebuffed. I felt embarrassed that one human being should be so dirty, so without dignity before another. There was a running sore at one corner of her mouth and a complete lack of intelligence in her eyes—nothing but the hurt, sycophantic expression of a dog who has been taught to beg. Even her gratitude at receiving the hundred-lire note I gave her was overacted, as her blessing was perfunctory.

No sooner had the girl left than the boy arrived, holding out an even dirtier, smaller paw and asking for cigarettes. Sibyl offered him chocolate, but either he had never seen the stuff or he had outgrown such childish tastes. He whined for cigarettes and in the end his cadging became so insistent that I had to put him firmly on the road, but still he would not go until a shout from the man took him scuttling after the pony and trap, frightened for his life.

The caravan turned the corner out of sight and I leaned back against the front wheel drinking the hot sweet tea and thinking of another gypsy. I had first seen him at a concert staged by the British Colony in Stockholm, and now, six years later, I could remember nothing of that evening except the appearance of the small swarthy man who had given a display of conjuring. His tricks had not been extraordinary and I would have forgotten him too had it not been for the speech he made. Sitting comfortably in the darkness of the auditorium I had suddenly realised that this man was talking about escaping from a prison camp in Germany, here in Stockholm, with Germans in the audience. Before I could protest one of the staff from the British Legation had walked on to the stage, made a hurried speech of thanks and effectively cut short the lecture. The next morning in the Legation they told me they were checking up on his escape. Messages were sent in various secret ways to various prison camps in Germany, replies were received; and the conjurer was sent to England by air, under escort.

I remember our chagrin that he had got home first. That night Mike and I had gone down to Bromma airport in an effort to persuade a BOAC pilot to fly us home. The weather had not been good and flying had been cancelled. I had jeered, saying that Bomber Command would be flying out that night, and it had ended with my offering to fight the duty pilot. I still blush to think of it.

Later in England we had learned the gypsy's story. He had never been to school and could neither read nor write. Born in a caravan, his loyalty was only to his band. He paid no taxes, owed no allegiance to the many countries through which he passed as a member of a travelling circus, but when war came he was conscripted into the army and captured at Dunkirk. He had no background to fortify him and no precedent to fit him for the fierce loyalty demanded of the prisoner of war. To sell the escape secrets of the other prisoners for food when neither the betrayed nor the buyer meant more to him than the other had been a natural thing. He had been discovered by his fellow prisoners and by them condemned to death. He would have been executed, but he had run to his German masters and they, in unusual loyalty to him, had given him a ticket to neutral Sweden.

The traitor was now in prison because his ethics were not those of the men who had sent him there. He was lucky not to have been shot. For those who should know better betrayal is the ultimate crime, but it was a crime for which, to this man, ignorance was full excuse. Soon he would be out again, out on the road, in the freedom of the open sky. Would he roam the world again occasionally remembering, but never understanding his two different spells of captivity? Or would he be ruined, urban, an indoor man unable ever again to leave the comfort of a cage?

Tired after the day's drive, tired from the traffic, smell and clamour of Rome followed by the dust and battering of the main road, I wanted nothing more than a place to put the car and a tiny patch of ground to pitch the tent. We drove inland until it was dark, crisscrossing the countryside on roads crowded with bullock-carts, traps, bicycles and people walking. One village ran into the next and every small patch of soil between was cultivated. Several times we turned down narrow lanes only to find deep, mosquito-ridden irrigation trenches on either side which forced us to back out again in the deep soft Italian darkness.

Once, alone in a small open aircraft above the clouds, without wireless or any link with living man, I had felt near-panic. Then it had seemed for a moment as though something awful were treading on my heels and that I must at all costs make contact with my own familiar world again, and that without delay. Now, in the teeming darkness, surrounded by people with whom I could not talk, whom I could not even see, I had a hint of the same isolation. "It's no good," I said, "let's admit we're beaten and go and get a room in Naples."

The drive into Naples took another two hours, through village after village whose people thronged the streets and whose open-fronted houses sent shafts of yellow light across the car, against a constant stream of empty bullock-carts returning from the city and cyclists without lamps. The air was filled with the tolling of bullock bells, the tinkling of bicycle bells and an occasional blast of a pneumatic horn as a lorry belonging to some co-operative lumbered home.

Our room in the hotel was high and cool with tall windows whose latticed shutters filtered the electric light from the street outside. There was a broken crystal chandelier, a marble floor and a picture of the moon above the Bay of Naples.

It was quiet there high above the street. I lay in the long bath, my heels resting on the smooth porcelain of the rounded edge, the cool water lapping my chest, remembering the first bath in Sweden after my return from Germany. It had been my first for a year and I had been scrubbed by a woman. The Municipal Baths had been like a prison, with duckboards on the floor and a large slab of yellow soap smelling of disinfectant. The water had been hot and plentiful, but it had all been ruined by this hefty woman in a white overall who had come in to soap our backs. Later, when I had my first real unhurried bath in Stockholm, it had been a luxury. Then I had sworn that it would always be like this, it would always be a new, exciting and cherished thing. I had learned that happiness lay in the complete realisation of one's present being. To say, Now I am having a bath; to know it with every sense, was to be utterly content. To bathe and at the same time think of something else was not.

But a man cannot keep his mind at rest, even in a hot bath, and I thought of Stockholm and the seven weeks I had spent there living in luxury but not yet free. I had been more restless in Sweden than in the prison camp. In Germany there had been the enemy, unity in a common cause; above all the vaulting horse with the dark tunnel below it which grew longer every day. For months my life had been occupied with vaulting, digging, working on my cover story and cherishing all the time the secret of that smelly burrow which would lead me to the outside world. Stockholm was not the outside world. The Swedish people were hospitable, almost too hospitable for three men who had come from such a monastic life. Mike and I, reunited with Oliver after our separate journeys, had behaved badly in many ways, drinking far too much, attending as many as three or four parties in the same evening and confusing our hosts by exchanging names and Services. Sometimes we had pretended to be Germans and on one occasion, gatecrashing a German party, had been forced to fight our way out. The members of the Legation had been very patient but we had wanted to get back to England and, pleasant though it was, the half way house of neutrality was not the goal.

It had taken some time to settle down even in England. Then Mike had gone to Italy and I had taken the pilot's course they had said I was too old to take when the war had started. We had seen more of one another when the war was over and Mike was back at Oxford. His sense of humour had helped a lot in these last few months when the three of us had been guests of honour at the literary parties. Oliver's book was nearly finished now and Mike, restless as ever, was in Malaya as a cadet in the Colonial Service after toying with the idea of Publishing and Soap. One look at a soap factory had been enough to cure him of a desire to shine in industry, and he had not been so sure about publishing after a few of the literary parties.

I thought of the narrow streets and open overcrowded hovels we had passed along the road. The people in these villages seemed content. Their religion gave them hope of after life, a promise of celestial glory which would more than compensate them for their present squalor, but there was more to it than that. Communal living seemed to give them a security and satisfaction which blinded them to everything outside. A man would finish work, in his own house, and would then sit outside that same house in the cool of the evening. A man would spend days, weeks, never moving from the same street. Girls would play in the street, grow up and parade that same street in the darkness of the evening. They would marry in that street and bear their children there. There were no secrets in the street, everything was known. If a man left the street for any length of time he would feel uneasy.

There had been the same contentment in a way in the prison camp. We would go for days, weeks, without contact with anyone except our own room-mates. A man's room was his home and anyone from any other room was foreign. He would sit outside that room in the evening and at night sleep there in security. If for some escape plan he had to sleep in another room he would be restless, and he was not happy until he was back in his own bed. From this parochial outlook the small square barbed-wire compound had seemed much bigger and when I came to leave it the world outside had seemed at times too big. Physical restriction had been an excuse for ambition sleeping, and sleeping ambition meant peace of mind.

If a man in one of these villages was ambitious he too could escape. He would sacrifice the warm protection of his squalor for the cold harshness of the outer world. But would he be much happier?

CHAPTER TEN

THE STREETS were not yet hot but the shopkeepers were sprinkling the pavements under the awnings with water from Chianti bottles as I waited for Sibyl outside the Post Office. Naples was crowded with people hurrying to work and overcrowded tramcars swayed and ground their way along the worn-out rails. Above the exhaust smoke of the cars I could distinguish the sharp ammoniacal smell of the horses which stood on the cab rank some distance down the street. Gradually the hum of traffic and the clatter of heels on paving stones merged into a dull murmur and, sitting there comfortably, my bare arm stretched along the pleasantly warm cellulose of the car door, I dozed.

I was awakened by the touch of a finger on my arm. A boy was there, a small dark good-looking boy. His hair was cut in a straight line above large brown eyes that regarded me with grave concern. When he saw that he had my full attention he whispered, "*Signore!*", and pointed to the rear wheel on the driver's side.

Thinking that a tyre was flat I leaned over the side of the cutaway door to look, putting out my left hand to support myself against the back of Sibyl's seat. I felt the strap of the camera case which was lying on the seat move gently under my hand. I grabbed hard and tried to turn, my hips wedged between the steering wheel and the seat. There was a scurry of footsteps and by the time I had struggled free the boy and his accomplice were running down the street.

The passers-by still clicked hurriedly to work. Only I, the nearly lost camera dangling from my grasp, seemed at all put out by this attempt at highway robbery. I hesitated a moment longer, then shouted and ran after the boys, pushing my way through the crowd on the pavement. But it was hopeless. Before I was half way down the street the boys had vanished. I turned and hurried back to the car, thinking of the leather mapcase which had been lying on the floor at Sibyl's feet. That too had vanished.

I waited for her, knowing full well what she was entitled to say. She came down the steps, cool and brown and capable in a light tan cotton frock, her hair falling loosely to her shoulders. She waved an envelope in her hand. "It's come," she called, "but I can't feel any notes inside."

"I've lost the mapcase." I told her of the camera and the boys.

"You saved the camera anyway," she said. "There was only one map in the case, and I'd much rather have them loose. Let's open this and see what he says."

I handed back the envelope which gave off a strong odour of cheap perfume. "You can read it as we go," I said. "Let's get out of this place before the spare wheel's pinched."

Up on the high narrow Autostrada which joins Naples to Pompeii Sibyl translated:

> *Monsieur, You will be without doubt surprised at receiving this letter. I am Madame Morino and it is I who have had your two letters which have strongly surprised and pained me. My husband has left the house since some days and I do not know where he finds himself now. Monsieur, excuse me if I importune you but I am going to explain to you my situation in some words—I am ill and come from a sanatorium. I have three infants of a low age the most young is one year—is it my illness which has affected my husband but he is no longer the same since I have been so ill—he who is of a nature very gentle has become brusque and wicked with me, his three little ones and with his old father and his old mother who live with us, he does not remind himself of anything any longer and at moments I ask myself if he has all his good sense. We are in a situation very painful but I will do my best after I can dispose of some things to send you it. Do be charitable for my children and for me Monsieur I will be grateful of it all my life—Do send me my Livret de Mariage which is so necessary to me for my affairs—and let me know what is passed with my husband. In the hope that you will wish to have pity on my three small ones and on myself—I beg you to believe my profound recognition and sincere gratitude—Marie Morino.*

Sibyl folded the letter and put it in her handbag. "Poor woman. Let's send her something."

I looked at her, frankly amazed. "Send her something? What do you mean?"

"Well, I mean send her Livret back and a few francs to help her along. It's obviously nothing to do with her."

"You've a lot to learn about life yet," I told her. "The way he pinched the coffee was confidence trick number one. Now, in the second lesson, we have confidence trick number two."

"You mean he hasn't left her?"

"I mean he probably dictated the letter."

"Do you really think so?"

"I wouldn't be a bit surprised. Notice that she asks for the Livret and then she will send the money. Also it seems strange to me that if he'd left her, as she says, he should have had the Livret with him. It was no use to him. But even if he had, it doesn't make much difference to her whether he's got it or we have. It's probably safer with us."

"But how will she get on without it? She says it's necessary for her affairs."

"Of course she can get on without it. Life doesn't stop because she's lost her Livret de Mariage. Dozens of people must lose them every day. There's bound to be some method of getting a temporary one."

"What's the next move?" She sounded only half-convinced.

"We'll think it over. . . ." I turned down off the Autostrada and saw the milling crowds outside the entrance to Pompeii, the coachloads of visitors, the touts, attendants, vendors of trinkets, mementoes and picture postcards, the groups of lounging men and boys who seemed to have no other purpose than to gaze at the people who had come to gaze. "The question is, will it be safe to leave the car here?"

"I'll sit here in the shade," Sibyl said, "and study the live Italians while you study the dead ones."

"Well don't study them too closely." I remembered Lambert and Morino and shuddered to think of their Neapolitan equivalent. "Don't you talk to anyone," I said.

There were steps leading to a counter where I paid the entrance fee, then more steps and a sloping path to the site of the ancient city. At the top of the path there was a waiting room and a kiosk where guide books and photographs were sold.

"You want a guide, mister?" The speaker was an elderly man wearing a tropical linen suit and a black homburg hat. He was short and looked unhealthy, and I could tell from two yards away that this digestion was not good. "You just go to the office and tell them you engage me. You want to see a representative section of Pompeii? I know how to give you a good idea of the city in the shortest time. I take you to the most interesting places, eh?" He moved closer and touched my arm. "I show you the brothel—everything." The other parties were moving off. "Come with me," the guide said. "I take you round the other way, not with party. You pay me afterwards. All the interesting things are locked."

As a boy I had read *The Last Days of Pompeii.* I had forgotten most of the book but had been left with a deep admiration for the Roman soldier who had stayed at his post when all were fleeing and had died there, standing upright in the mountain ash. Now, standing outside the Forum, looking at the decapitated stone pillars and mutilated statues, I might have been in Unter den Linden by the Brandenburger Tor. The only thing missing was the Russian war memorial. And walking through the quiet streets with their paved sidewalks and rows of houses cut off at the first storey or sliced in half, I thought how impressive this must have been for visitors before the Second World War, and how commonplace to us. The fact that these ruins were a couple of thousand years old made them, to me, no more venerable than the ruins of Coventry, Warsaw or Berlin.

For the guide, however, the age of the city seemed the important thing. That so long ago people should have made bread, sold wine in shops, warned their neighbours to beware of the dog, appeared extraordinary to him. He pointed out the cart ruts in the cobbles, the worn steps, the stumps of trees which, covered by the protecting ash for nearly two thousand years, looked newly felled. He described the shops we passed, the markets, theatres, public baths with running hot and cold water; and as the old man talked I found myself being caught in the spell of this ancient city, wanting to know more about the people who had lived in these houses which resembled modern villas rather than anything designed during the intervening centuries. The houses of the wealthy had a central court open to the sun, sometimes paved, sometimes laid out in flower-beds, but always with a fountain or stream of running water.

In one of the finest houses there was a mural painting behind locked shutters opened only for male visitors. I had seen similar drawings of equal artistic merit on the walls of public conveniences in many countries and their influence had been pointed out by art masters in the moulding of a classical cornice. The design shape was fundamental and I saw no reason for the lock and key. There were similar motifs incised in the stonework above a door or over a baker's oven, but these were stylised and scarcely recognisable for what they were.

Now the guide indicated a direction sign in the form of an extended phallus cut deeply into the stone of the road surface and I realised that the end of the tour was in sight. The house was locked and a uniformed attendant stood by the door. We waited in the street as men must have waited thousands of years before. "Pompeii was nearer the coast then," the guide said. "The sea lapped the gate of the city and ships unloaded here. The sign in the pavement was for the sailors who didn't speak Latin."

When the door opened a party of American sailors filed out. They were young and the stiff embarrassed expression on their faces was as uniform as their crew-cut and their clean white ducks. The attendant held open the door and one by one as the sailors came out they handed him three cigarettes. I wondered where, in the building or beforehand, the sailors had decided on the fee. Or had it been stipulated by their guide?

The interior was divided into a number of small cell-like rooms, each with a short couch made of masonry. On the walls of the entrance hall were crude paintings of the various attitudes of love. "It's like I told you," the guide said, "some of the sailors who came here couldn't speak Latin so they pointed to the one they wanted." And as we stood there I felt across the centuries the humanity of the people who had built this city. I thought of the young sailor who could not speak Latin, hesitating before the pictures, unable to decide which one to choose.

The rear wheels were barely off the road but we were in the shade. As the cars streamed past, I sat sipping the half-sparkling acid-tasting Chianti and watched Sibyl make sandwiches from the flat heavy loaf of Italian bread and the thin floppy slices of pink, peppercorned mortadella. "Where are they all going?" I said. "What are they all doing?"

"The same as we are, I expect. Trying to get away from the crowds."

"It'll be like this all along the coast. It's senseless condemning ourselves to it just to be by the sea."

"What about the fishing?"

"Damn the fishing." For hours now we had been driving along the winding coast road, the cliff on one side and a high wall of mountain on the other. Roadmaking was in progress and once we had waited in a long queue while men dynamited huge masses of rock out of the mountainside. Before and after us cars had fretted and puthered exhaust fumes into the vibrating air and the moment the signal was given the restive conveyor belt had surged forward along the debris-littered road through a choking cloud of dust. All morning we had been driving with and against a tide of cars and motor-scooters, screaming tyres, tooting horns and stinks of exhaust. There had been no time to admire the view, talk or even think. My whole attention had been on keeping my place in the hectic procession which was chasing from one end of the Italian coastline to the other in both directions. I took the map from the front seat of the car. "We can leave the coast road in Salerno and get up into the hills. If we begin to drive north now, up the centre of Italy, we'll have more time in the Abruzzi and Tuscany. The coast is all right if you hire a villa or stay in an hotel but it's hopeless for campers."

"There were one or two places," Sibyl said. "The pinewood at Follonica for instance."

"You couldn't swim there, and that place near Portofino where we met the smuggler chap was just pure luck."

We had stopped once earlier in the morning at a bend in the road, attracted by a sign which read EMERALD GROTTO, and had climbed a steep winding staircase down the face of the cliff to a landing stage where a boatman waited. He had rowed us across the small cove and through a narrow opening into an underground creek where stalactites hanging from the roof glowed redly in the light of his lantern. The grotto itself was illuminated from underwater, the sunlight striking down through the surface of the sea outside and entering through a submarine opening in the wall of the cliff. This filtered light striking upwards again through the clear green water was reflected in rippling colour on the stone of the cavern roof, and when the boatman had struck the water with his oar the splash had splintered light into a thousand coloured fragments.

In the grotto the air had been cool and fresh but back on the road again, hot and sticky after the climb up the cliff, we had quickly lost the memory of floating on a translucent lake of fire and longed only for somewhere in the shade to eat our lunch. At last we had pulled off and parked next to a neat geometrical heap of stones painted with a broad diagonal band of whitewash, which the roadmakers had left under a parched olive tree.

"The Germans used to paint their coal heaps like that to stop us stealing it," I told Sibyl. "It's funny how war legalises theft and murder. . . . I wonder what these two characters want."

The men with the Lambretta had been hovering for some time, laughing and tinkering with their machine, edging nearer and nearer to the parked Bentley. Now, catching my eye, they pushed the Lambretta right up to our table and sat there, unashamedly staring.

"*Buon giorno!*" I walked right into it as usual.

"*Bella machina!*" One of the men, dark and dashing with two rows of incredibly white teeth below a black pencil-line moustache, caressed the radiator of the car. "*Gasolina?*" He wore a yachting cap, a blue jersey and a red handkerchief knotted round his neck.

"*Si, gasolina.*" I thought he was asking whether it ran on petrol or diesel oil.

He unscrewed the filler-cap of his tank and shook the machine significantly, to show that there was no sound of swishing petrol. "*Niente gasolina!*"

"Well I'm damned, they're trying to cadge petrol now."

"Maybe they'll go away if we give them some," Sibyl said.

I took the spare tin from the back of the car and poured half the contents into the motor scooter. "*Niente olio,*" I warned them. The driver grinned. "The engine will probably seize up," I told Sibyl. "It's a two-stroke. Oil should be mixed with the petrol."

"I expect they've stolen it. I shouldn't worry."

The Lambretta's passenger, who was dressed in mechanic's overalls, had approached the Bentley on hands and knees and was vigorously shaking one of the front wheels as though he hoped it would come away in his hands. "*Bella machina,*" he said, "*bella machina!*" He stopped shaking and began to examine the steering mechanism with the preoccupied air of an expert. The whole act was so clear that it made me laugh. In gratitude for the petrol he would, if it were necessary, repair the car. But it was not necessary. Had one of the wheels been falling off, a dangerous thing on these steep hills, he would have put the matter right free of charge. As it was, the car was perfect and there was nothing he could do. He gave the front wheel one last violent shake, cleaned his hands on the seat of his overalls and squatted on his heels a few inches away from the table. His companion, astride the Lambretta, sat waiting.

"*Sigarètta!*"

"*Niente sigarètta,*" I said. I was damned if they were going to cadge cigarettes too. Those we had brought were for Germany.

The overalled one looked winning and made the motions of puffing a cigarette. "*Sigarètta!*"

"We don't smoke."

The tone of my voice must have been understood because the man shrugged his shoulders at the uselessness of a foreigner who could not produce a cigarette and pulled out a crushed packet of Lucky Strike.

"Lambert must have been round here," Sibyl said.

"Probably a couple of the gang. I expect he's got stooges all along the coast."

The yachting one started the engine with a splutter, the overalled one climbed on to the pillion and the motor-scooter buzzed erratically away in the direction of Naples, its high waspish note hanging on the air.

"That reminds me," Sibyl said, "we must write to Madame Morino."

Dear Madame [we wrote], *Your letter, which I received in Naples, has occasioned me some difficulty. If it is true that you are in the situation you describe, then I ought to send you your Livret de Mariage at once. Unfortunately your husband has duped me once already and I am naturally suspicious that it was in fact he who dictated your letter and that it is nothing more than a ruse. Your husband promised my wife in Nice that he would sell certain of our things. She was trusting enough to let him go and he disappeared with our possessions. It was only by chance that his Livret de Mariage came into my hands and I discovered his address. You will appreciate that the Livret de Mariage is now my only means of recovering the price of the things that your husband stole from us. It is arranged with the office of the British Consul in Nice that if I do not receive at least half of the 10,000 francs by return of post addressed to me at Poste Restante, Milano, I shall send him the Livret de Mariage. He will hand it to the Chief of Police with my charge of theft against your husband. If I receive at least half of the money in Milano, I assure you that I will send you your Livret de Mariage and your husband will be free. I would add that I know the names and addresses of the people who were in the café where your husband stole my things and who will be witnesses for me. It is not my wish that you should make a sacrifice to send me the money. If you have not seen your husband the Chief of Police will doubtless send you your Livret de Mariage after I have reported the theft.*

"That should shake him," I said.

"She may still love him. I hope she doesn't starve the kids to send the money."

"You still think she's genuine?"

"I don't know."

"Look," I said, "we'll send the Livret back. It's not worth it if it's going to worry you."

"No, send the letter. We're only asking for half what the coffee's worth."

"That's the girl. We mustn't let him get away with it. We'll send him a reminder every day from now on. It's the dripping water that wears away the stone. We'll reduce him to a gibbering mass of fear before we've finished."

Late in the evening we turned off the road on to a broad stony path which led to the edge of a wood where the grass was short and clean and studded with flowers. We were hidden from the road by a swelling field of wheat, and through the wood of young oak and mountain ash there were tracks made by sheep or pigs. "How's this?"

"Perfect."

"I'll just pull round so that we can get the tent between the trees and the car." I let in the clutch and we moved forward. There was a jarring crash and then a rending sound. It seemed that whatever we had hit was tearing my belly as it tore at the vitals of the car. I jumped down. A rock, projecting nearly a foot from the ground, had dented the crankcase and torn the oil shield. It was securely jammed. I crouched there looking for the tell tale stream of black oil, but none came. "I don't think we've done any real damage."

"It sounded horrible."

I was angry with myself, angry that I should be tired enough to be so careless. The rock was there plain for anyone to see. "I'll have to jack her up."

"Do it in the morning. Let's just relax and drink some wine. Then I'll cook you a steak."

"We'll stop earlier in future. There's no point in pressing on like this. It's not as though we were in a race." I reached into the back of the car for the flask of Chianti and filled the steel tumblers. I handed one to Sibyl and drank deeply from mine. "We were hot and now we are cool. We were thirsty and now we drink. If instead of rushing around putting up the tent and cooking a meal we just sit and appreciate, we shall have achieved something."

"We shan't have achieved the tent or the meal," she said. "I'd rather sit and appreciate with a meal inside me and the tent up and the beds made."

"We'll finish our drinks first anyway. Then I'd better jack the old thing up. I can't leave her on a rock all night."

We had driven far since we had left the coast, enjoying the freshness of the air and the freedom of the long empty road and wide expanse of golden hills. The sky was high and pale blue with small puffs of white cloud and the evening light had clarity and warmth. The air here was no longer heavy and moisture laden, softening the outline of objects seen in the distance and soiling everything it touched with the grime and pollution of the towns. Here there were no mosquitoes, no insistent murmur of cicadas to give the night a restless urgency that fired the blood and made one conscious of the teeming life in the plain below. Here the air was clear and cold and the landscape of wheatfields and forest and rock was hard and pure in colour.

CHAPTER ELEVEN

WE AWOKE early to the song of a skylark and the voices of peasants who were walking along the footpath close to the tent. I lay listening to the warm rough country dialect and the sound of church bells from across the valley. There was a feeling of Sunday in the air.

We ate breakfast to the steady ringing of the bells. Scattered groups of peasants were still passing, dressed in stiff holiday clothes, all making their way along the edge of the wood to the village on the hill. When the bells stopped ringing there was the report of a gun and faintly, borne on the wind, the strains of a brass band. Through the clear air across the valley there was the glint of sun on metal and a tiny splash of colour as a procession wound its way along the ramparts.

"Say, you folks British?" The speaker was a solid man of middle age dressed incongruously in a light grey lounge suit with wide sloping shoulders and a broad-brimmed fedora. He detached himself from a group of peasants who hesitated on the path, obviously impressed by his knowledge of the foreign language.

"Good morning," I said. "What's happening up there on the hill?"

"It's a feast day, Corpus Christi. The folks here make a lot of it."

"Are you over here on holiday?"

"No, I'm back for good. Bought myself a plot of land. I went to the States thirty years ago but now I guess I'm home again."

"It's lovely here," Sibyl said.

The man looked round him at the hills, the wide blue sky, as though seeing them for the first time. "It's a lovely country all right, but it's so goddamned poor. I guess I'd forgotten how folks lived here, when I was in the States. You're the first folks I've spoken English to, since I've been back. . . . Oh well, must be getting along. Promised my old Momma I'd be there." He waved his hand and, uncomfortable in city shoes, hurried after his companions now some distance down the path. Suddenly he stopped and turned. "I guess I should have stayed."

We broke camp and drove by the roundabout road to the old weather-beaten town perched on the edge of a low cliff down which the refuse of ages was splashed like the droppings of a giant bird. The procession was over and there was a street market in full swing.

I walked through the steep narrow streets connected by flights of steps so that they were impassable for wheeled traffic, and thought of the ruins of Pompeii. The streets were paved in the same way but in Pompeii there had been sidewalks, while here they were unnecessary. The chariots of Pompeii must have been more lethal than the donkeys of this town. I stopped at the door of the church and stood watching the solemn ceremonial which I did not understand. The vestments glowed in the dark interior of the church and the slow movements of the ritual and the clicking of the censers were carried out with grave exactitude. I thought of the monastery I had once visited in England. How easy in a way to shelve responsibility, to bury oneself in a community, work and sing and pray. The price? One or two of the pleasures of the flesh.

I stopped again by a man who sat by the side of the road selling knives. They were razor sharp and the blade folded into a handle made of horn and carved with a simple pattern. There was a stylised flower incised on the blade, and the knife was well-balanced and fitted comfortably in the hand. I tried several, all were slightly different, and bought the one I liked best as a present for Sibyl. Back at the car, I found her surrounded.

"I know what you've been doing," she said. "You've been into the church and you've bought a razor."

"So that's what it is. I thought it was pretty sharp. How did you know?"

"Mr Amodio told me." She indicated an elderly man at the forefront of the crowd, pressed hard up against the mudguard. "My husband," she said to him.

"How do you do?" I said.

"You gotta a sigarètta?"

"Sorry, I don't smoke."

"You donta chew either?"

"Sorry."

"Mr Amodio has been in America," Sibyl explained.

"Oh really?" I turned to the man. "I was in New York myself for a short time."

"I was in Chicago. Sure wish I was backa there now."

"Why don't you go?"

"Cause I was deported, see? They gotta the screws on me a'ri', a'ri'."

"Mr Amodio was running hooch," Sibyl said.

"Thisa place no good." He spat on the cobbles of the square. "No goddam civilisation here. They don't know they're alive."

I looked round at the hard tanned faces of the peasants and then at Mr Amodio.

"There's not even a proper saloon in the place. A man can't even buy a coke. And they have a movie once a month." He spat again, narrowly missing the front wheel. "Where you sleep tonight, eh? Roma? Napoli?"

"We're going north. We came to see the procession but we seem to be too late."

"Thisa small town, no good. You wanna go Campobasso for gooda festa."

"Where?"

"Campobasso, nexta big town north from here." He pointed to the main road we had left. "Campobasso, bigga processione, bigga festa, mucha people!"

"Campobasso, Campobasso," the crowd affirmed, "Campobasso!"

Slowly we inched our way out of the square, descended again to the main road and headed north, passing more and more people all heading in the direction of Campobasso. There were whole families on foot in their best clothes, parties of schoolchildren led by cassocked priests, young people on bicycles, cartloads of gypsies; everyone laughing and talking and greeting one another with excitement.

Driving on the crowded road I remembered another feast day, two years before, in Brittany. We were making our way towards the Bay of Douarnenez, hoping to camp on the sand dunes by the beach. It was on this road that we began to meet the hikers, as we had today, all travelling in the same direction, towards the coast. Sibyl had been doubtful about the possibility of camping. "It must be some popular holiday resort. Do you think we should go back?"

But I wanted to go on and drew up by a perspiring couple who were pushing their bicycle up the hill. "Ask them if they know a good place to camp."

The cyclist replied quickly, as though they were expecting the question, "Santannaypalou!" and pointed up the hill. Not understanding, we stopped again by two young men in business suits, walking with rucksacks on their backs. "Santannaypalou!" they said and pointed up the road.

The next time we asked a young priest in charge of a tribe of schoolboys wearing grey pinafores. "Santannaypalou!", a chorus of pointing arms. We drove on.

"I've got it," Sibyl said at last. "It must be a saint. Saint Anne La Palud. *Paludisme* is malaria—marshes perhaps. We're probably going to a shrine."

The hikers became more and more numerous and now there were horses and carts, caravans and giant motor coaches. I had given up all hope of a quiet beach and was pressing forward to see what had brought all these people to this lonely place. We turned down a narrow lane signposted SAINT ANNE LA PALUD and found ourselves in the middle of a funfair. There were coconut shies, shooting booths, fortune-tellers, and behind them roundabouts, swings, mat slides and cakewalks. There was the rumble of machinery, the scream of voices, the strident blare of steam organs.

We followed the now densely packed streams of cars, cyclists and hikers through the middle of the fair, through the dust and smell, over an earth track and out on to the dunes at the edge of the sea, clean windswept hills of sand, pale yellow in the evening light with green fringes of marram grass and the distant thunder of surf. The dunes had once been fortified. There was a row of derelict pillboxes along their highest contour but these had been scoured by wind and sand, bleached by the sun until they had become part of the sandy shore. There were tents of all colours and all sizes from small bivouacs like our own to huge marquees. Some were pitched singly as far as possible from their neighbours, others were set in groups, huddled together like a bedouin camp. We pitched ours to one side of the track, as near to the sea as we could get. Behind us when the daylight faded, small fires, torches, even candles were lit in the surrounding encampments, until the darkness was studded with flickering points of light. We too lit a fire, from driftwood, which burned hotly, spitting blue from the salt. The glow from the fire lit up the interior of the tent and we sat cross-legged in the sand listening to 'Pistol-packin' Momma', refined by the distance, come faintly from the roundabout behind the dunes. Slowly I became aware of another tune, a low dirge, wordless, endlessly repeating the same simple phrase, plaintive in the night.

"What's that?"

"What?" She poked the fire with a piece of driftwood and pushed it into the heart of the blaze. The sudden flame lit up her face, full of solemn enjoyment as she tended the fire. There are not many things she likes better than lighting fires, any sort of fire so long as it is in the open air. The acrid smell of the smoke, the light on her face, the clean salt tang of the sand on which the tent was pitched all blended together into a moment of happiness. Then I heard it again, faintly on the wind.

"That tune—listen!" The chanting seemed to grow louder, to swell and then to fade on the night air. I pulled on my boots. "I'm going to see."

"I'm coming too." She took her windbreaker from the seat of the car (not the Bentley then but an even older car, a two-seater Morris I had bought for sixty pounds when I was in the RAF), and we climbed the dunes away from the sea. The sound of chanting grew, fierce and insistent. Equally insistent, but fainter now, was the refrain of 'Pistol-packin' Momma' played by the steam organ at the fair. From the brow of the dunes we were able to see the flat hinterland spread at our feet like a black velvet cloth, jewelled with fires and torches, patterned by the beams of head-lamps and scattered with glowing ruby tail-lights. Behind and above, like a halo, was the haze of light from the fair. In the centre was the church. Its steeple, floodlit by lamps set at the level of the belfry, seemed to stand in mid-air without support. Towards this steady light crept slowly writhing snakes of flickering torches. Faintly on the evening breeze came the elusive smell of incense.

The steam organ was suddenly silent and we could hear the chanting of a thousand voices as the pilgrims neared the church. We picked our way down the hill in the darkness, gradually distinguishing the reiterated plea of their incantation. '*Santez Anna, nos padrones. . . .*' The two robed figures bearing the relics in a casket, followed by the clergy, led the converging processions in through the door of the church. Each pilgrim held a candle protected by a paper shield. There was a fresh wind and the followers had difficulty in keeping the candles burning. Some were constantly re-lighting from their neighbours, others with their candles dead and useless in their hands walked on in darkness. '*Nos bénédictions s'élèvèr-ent. . . .*'

Outside in the open air the singing had seemed merely picturesque. Here in the church with the smell of incense and the concentration of the crowd it had swollen into a powerful force. The words I could not understand, but the rhythm of the constantly repeated phrase beat on my brain. What were the pilgrims seeking? For what favour or protection did they plead? The relics of the saint lay in an ornate casket, while from the wall of the church the tortured Christ looked down on the rising incense and the smoke from the burning candles. '*Santez Anna, santez Anna. . . .*' I looked round me at the foreign faces; weatherbeaten fisherman, stolid peasant, slim dark student, business man in blue suit, hiker in shorts. Did they really believe that the saint would intercede? Some, engrossed in their missals, telling their beads, mumbling to themselves, were probably devout. On the faces of many was an expression I had seen on the faces of teenage youngsters gathered in the gramophone department of the Liverpool store, listening to a record of Frank Sinatra.

Sibyl pulled at my sleeve. "Let's go to the fair," she said.

We walked on down the hill, the cheerful secular music from the steam organ superseding the mournful plea for forgiveness, or whatever it was. The air was thick with dust and smoke, trembling with the blare of reed and brass. The night was brilliantly alive and loud with the music and the laughter and screams of people enjoying themselves.

And now, on the way to Campobasso and remembering Douarnenez, I said, "Let's give it a miss, shall we? One procession's very much like another. What about pushing up into the Abruzzi?"

"Good," she said. "We might see the wolves."

"What wolves?"

"The wolves of the Abruzzi. They still have them there. I've always wanted to see a wolf."

And she probably would. She has a facility for getting into

trouble and for pulling me in after her. I remembered the morning after that other fête at Douarnenez. We had tried to avoid the fair by taking a short cut across the wide sands which looked so safe and firm but were in fact dangerous; but they had not been signposted because the war had only just finished and the French had not got round to it. We were half way across when the car began to settle. The running-boards saved her for a while but she was sinking fast, and I could see my cherished car, my sole wealth, vanishing from view. I leaped out and rushing back across the sand to the nearest holidaymakers shrimping on the rocks, yelling to them "*Assistez-moi! Assistez-moi!*" I collected a small crowd and returned to the car, to find Sibyl gone. We pushed and heaved but only forced the Morris deeper into the engulfing sand. Then she appeared with a farmer and two strong horses, and the car was saved.

When the farmer had been rewarded and the holidaymakers thanked we crawled in our bathing costumes underneath the car and cleaned off the oily sand, and as we went down to the sea to clean ourselves I asked her to marry me.

We came to a tall grey village clinging to the side of a hill so that no house faced another but looked instead across the rocky valley to the mountains. Doors and windows were heavily barred. "We'll have to knock someone up," Sibyl said. "We've absolutely nothing to eat. I'd forgotten it's a feast day."

I sat in the car in the quiet street while she explored the village. She came back with a loaf of bread. "We're lucky," she said. "I asked a small boy who happened to be the baker's son. He took me home and the baker unlocked the shop."

"Any luck with the butcher?"

"I'm going back to the baker. He sent his son for the butcher. We'll eat tonight after all."

I looked out across the valley to the grey and violet mountain on the other side. The air was clear and the village silent. It was high afternoon and I imagined everyone behind those ventilated shutters sleeping until evening. The builders of lidos and the strewers of wastepaper had not yet found this part of Italy. Here in the Abruzzi shepherds still guarded their flocks against the wolves which roamed in packs and sometimes came down into the villages in their winter hunger. A boy clipclopped past, seated comfortably on a donkey whose dainty feet raised a small cloud of dust which hung on the still air.

Then the quiet afternoon was rent by the tearing-calico noise of a Lambretta travelling at speed. I turned in time to see a dark good-looking youth scoot by with a windswept laughing Sibyl on the pillion. I decided that she would be safe enough on a motor-scooter, in a place like this, but the next ten minutes dragged until she came, carrying a neat bundle wrapped in a newspaper. "Lamb chops."

"Who's the boy friend on the Lambretta?"

"The butcher. He took me from the baker's to his shop, but I walked back. They're wonderful, those Lambrettas."

"What are the chops like?"

"They're wonderful too."

We pushed on deeper into the wild country of the Abruzzi. Here the red roofs of the low cream-washed houses were held down by huge boulders. Every building was low-pitched and securely anchored to the ground. Only the fields were steeply sloping and small, and full of wild flowers. It was uphill all the way and the golden rock began to show more and more through the surface soil. The roadside trees were stunted and the wind came in sudden gusts round the mountain ridges, whipping up the dust and bellying the canvas cover on the car. "It's going to be a job to pitch the tent," I shouted.

Sibyl was studying the map, holding it under the dashboard out of the wind. "We're coming to a pass, the Devil's Pass. It may be sheltered there."

We passed a gypsy encampment by the side of the road, the gaily painted caravans tightly shuttered. To our left we could see the upper peaks of the mountains now shrouded in dark cloud. A heavy mist, almost rain, sat coldly on the wind. The country which earlier had been gold and blue was blue and violet-grey, the ceiling only a few feet above our heads.

It was not until we reached the pass that we were able to find a flat place where we could pull off the road. Here was a patch of level grass dotted with wild lavender, scabious and clover, through which the river tumbled whitely. I drove down a steep embankment on to the field and drew close under its shelter but the wind was strong even here, and I collected boulders from the river to weigh down the guy-ropes and anchor the flapping brailing to the ground. There was a burned circle of grass surrounded by wisps of straw, horse droppings and thin chips of wood from whittled sticks. "It looks as though we chose the only possible spot for miles," I said. "I hope they don't come along and say we pinched their place."

"Who?"

"Gypsies. This must be a regular halt for them."

"They won't come along this time of night will they? They'll all be sleeping near the towns on a feast day."

"No—anyway they'd have bedded down long ago on a night like this. It's only amateurs who get caught out in the Devil's Pass when it's all set to blow a gale."

I drove the car a bit nearer and took a rope from her over the top of the tent to the ground on the other side; if we took off in the night we would take the car with us. Sibyl was already frying the chops in the lee of the raised flap. "One day we'll take a holiday and just go," she said. "Not to get anywhere by any time, but just go for the sake of going. Travel like the gypsies in a horse-drawn caravan."

"Or with a donkey."

"You couldn't do it with a donkey these days. Stevenson stayed at hostelries where they had stabling and fodder. Imagine riding up to the door of a modern hotel and saying, 'Can I park my ass?'"

"They'd take you for an American," I said.

CHAPTER TWELVE

THE TONNEAU cover was across the seats but I had not put up the hood because of the wind, and a pool of water had collected on the canvas. I unfastened the press-studs and managed to tip most of the water on to the ground. The rest poured down the front of my trousers. There was only one way to pack, and now, in the cold driving rain, nearly every article must be taken out of the car, placed inside the tent and repacked in the right order. Before we were half way through the operation we, and most of our gear, were sodden.

At last everything was back in the car. The tent itself, heavy with water, we folded loosely and spread like the jam in a sandwich between the waterproof groundsheet and the tonneau cover. It was a full half hour before, soaked to the skin and hungry, we bumped and squelched off the muddy track up the embankment and on to the metal of the road. "They do it for pleasure," I said.

There were men working on the road, wild hairy men who ignored the rain and stood staring as the low black car splashed past. The youngest of them gave a long howl of appreciation when he saw Sibyl, rain- and wind-swept, laughing in the car. One of the wolves of the Abruzzi I thought, sourly.

The countryside was grey and brown, grey rocks, brown grass, brown lizards darting across the road. The mountains were volcanic, huge rounded boulders of larva, sudden jagged peaks thrust up and left towering like the petrified waves of an angry sea. There had been recent landslides and where the falls had been the rock was golden and glistened in the sun that shone fitfully between the showers. We came to a ruined village, the houses with nothing above the first floor, windows hanging, plaster peeling. Somehow it did not look like bomb damage, although I knew there had been a lot of fighting round here.

Mike had been fighting in these mountains, with light guns carried by pack-mules, and coloured troops as muleteers. That was after we had got back from Sweden and Oliver and I were still in England lecturing for MI9. I had gathered from Mike's letter that he found the campaign in Italy amusing. Wicked Captain Blackgloves. They had called him that because of his black leather gauntlets. His subtle mind had enjoyed the roundabout approach necessary in settling the day to day differences between his men. He would walk down the lines and find one of the troopers sulking in the sun instead of strapping. Ask him what is wrong, he would tell the interpreter. Sir, he say he has a devil in his belly. Ask him what the devil says. Sir, he say devil angry because his ration of hay was smaller than the others. Tell him that he will be given a larger ration tonight to make up for it. And Wicked Captain Blackgloves would walk on confident that the devil had been exorcised.

We passed more ruined deserted villages, crumbling back into the stone from which they had been built. The whole area seemed to have been lifted, split and torn, and the road was frequently buttressed against the sliding rock.

Beyond the pass we drove down through country which reminded me of the slate-quarrying districts of North Wales, the same bare rock and dust, the same great gashes in the earth's surface with small dust-covered stone shacks nestling beneath the sheer vertical face from which the rock had come, but here the dust was gold instead of grey. On our left below us was a queer flat depression in the hills, a huge plateau green with cultivation and intersected by a grid of narrow blue canals gleaming in the sun, bordered by rows of tall poplars which cast their morning shadows like the lines of hachuring across a map. The road led us zigzagging slowly downwards and the strange flat plain that had looked so much like a Persian carpet from above became three-dimensional. The strips of green-turning-to-gold were fields of wheat. There were fields of clover, vines and maize, all in long geometrical sections bordered by elder, now in flower, poplars and occasionally cypress trees.

The sun came out to stay and it was warm again. We lowered the hood when we stopped to draw water from a stone trough which had the date 1877 and a long inscription carved into its side. Behind the trough on the first easy slopes of the hill was another ruined village, and after spreading the tent to dry we walked through the empty street. In one of the biggest buildings men were sorting stone and arranging it in neat heaps.

"*Buon giorno*," I said.

"*Buon giorno*."

"What happened?" I swept my arm round to indicate the whole of the ruined village.

"*Terremoti*," one of the men explained, and held out his hands palm downwards, moving them from side to side. "*Terremoti!*"

"*Quando?*" It was one of the few Italian words I knew.

The man scratched some figures in the dust: 1915.

"They're long enough rebuilding it," I said.

"Perhaps they're not rebuilding it. Perhaps they're only collecting the stone for another village somewhere else."

"If so some archaeologist two thousand years hence is going to be very angry with them. It happened in Pompeii. Long after the earthquake there the local people took marble and other stones from the ruins and built their farms and houses with it. The guide thought they were vandals, but Pompeii was only an old ruin to them and I reckon they had every right to take a carved marble slab to floor their pigsty with. It shows a certain enterprise, and it's far better for the human race to go on and build new pigsties than mope over ancient ruins. . . . I wonder if he can tell us anything about this place." I called to the man and pointed to the plain below.

"*Lago*," he replied. "*Lago di Fucino!*"

"*Grazie*."

Another man cut in with a torrent of explanation which I could not understand. I said "*Grazie*" again, to stop him but I might as well have tried to cut short the earthquake which had destroyed the town. The man went on and on and I stood there, trying to look intelligent and not understanding a word, until he had finished. "*Grazie!*" I repeated, and added "*Arrivederci!*" in case he should start again.

"What was all that about?" Sibyl was studying the inscription on the stone water trough.

"He said it was a lake. Lake Fucino." Suddenly I remembered *Fontamara*, one of the first and probably the best of the many books about Italian villagers. The rich land in the bed of the dried lake had not brought them much comfort. "It was a lake once, that is. In the last century a banker from Rome nearly exhausted his fortune trying to drain it. But he managed it in the end and now it's the most fertile stretch of land in Italy."

"Did you understand all that?" The expression on her face gave me a supreme moment of being the linguist in the family, but I knew I couldn't keep it up.

I grinned. "Oh, there was a lot more than that. It was the largest lake in Italy until they drained it. Its history goes right back to the time of the Romans. The Emperor Claudius first tried to drain it. He thought he'd done it and he declared a Roman holiday. He had galleons built, armed twenty thousand slaves to man them and staged a naval battle on the lake. All the people came from Rome to watch the spectacle and to see the lake for the last time and Claudius and his wife, dressed in purple robes, sat on thrones on the hillside to watch the two navies wipe each other out. They'd lined the shores with the Imperial Guard so that the twenty thousand slaves shouldn't take it into their heads to stage a rebellion. Then when the battle was over and Claudius gave the signal to open the tunnel gates they found the channel wasn't deep enough, and the whole thing was a flop."

"Was that really what he said?"

"Of course it was."

"Right," she said. "You can do the shopping from now on."

I gave in.

By the time we had breakfasted and the tent was dry she had translated the trough's inscription word by word from the dictionary. *What Kings and Emperors have failed to do has been done by Alessandro Torlonia, Prince of this City, by the immensity of his mind and the force of money.*

From the plateau we climbed into the hills again. The golden rock was dotted with wild broom, draped with laburnum, festooned with traveller's joy. Dog roses thrust their long spiky arms through tangles of pink bindweed and the edges of the road were lined with poppies, lavender and tall rods of viper's bugloss. There were gangs of men at work, each gang under a foreman in uniform who did not work. The labourers were tall, young, good-looking men who, when they recognised the car as English, at once became beggars, thrusting out their hands and calling, "*Sigarètta, sigarètta!*"

"I wish they wouldn't beg," Sibyl said.

"It was the war," I said. "We all had too many cigarettes in the war."

"The war's been over some time now. If I could speak Italian I'd say to them, Do you want foreigners to think all Italians are beggars? I don't think they'd do it again."

"I'm sure they wouldn't. . . . We started it in the war. The troops dished out stuff with a free hand, when these young chaps were kids. Now they say 'Sigarètta' as a sort of greeting. They'd be astounded if I stopped and gave them one—probably don't smoke." I thought of the stiff uncomfortable line of sailors filing out of the brothel in Pompeii, each handing the guide three cigarettes, easing their embarrassment by dishing out the usual tip.

"If only the priests would tell them," Sibyl said.

"The Church teaches them humility, not pride. There's nothing in the Bible to tell you not to beg."

Pride, how the conformists hate it and attempt to stifle it. Pride of craftsmanship has almost vanished from industry, pride of independence from family life. If only those honest welfare workers would realise that whatever you give a man for nothing you take away an equivalent amount in pride or self-respect. *Take what you will, saith the Lord, but pay for it.* Free education, free meals, free medical service were given, as you thought free, but the price in lack of self-responsibility would be exacted in the end. The road from Boulogne had been lined with British students, Union Jacks sewn on to packs that were far too heavy for them to carry, thumbing lifts to the Riviera. They did not consider it begging. They would not have dreamed of hanging round Victoria station with an enamel cup and a placard round their necks begging the money to pay their fare; but this was different. It did not occur to them that if you travel with a spare seat in your car you may prefer it that way, that perhaps you did not welcome the idea of a stranger listening to your conversation. They thumbed lifts, and if you refused they showed their opinion of your selfishness. It used not to be like that. There was a time when an Englishman took pride in paying his way. This was one of the results of indiscriminate State charity. 'But you pay for it,' the theorists say, 'it's not free.' That sort of payment is too big a conception for the average man. To him it is free unless individual payment is made and individual effort made to save the cash with which to pay.

We sat on small iron chairs under an awning on the deserted terrace of the roadside café. The proprietor, a short stocky man, left his meal and hurried out to attend to us. We ordered spaghetti, grilled veal and salad, and red Chianti. It was cool under the faded pink-striped awning which slapped and pulled in the wind. The street below was white in the sun and small upright columns of dust swept across it.

The proprietor, assisted by a little girl, brought the spaghetti heaped on large pottery dishes. "You like spaghetti?" It was the first time he had spoken in English.

"Very much," I said. "You speak English." I said it categorically, for want of anything better.

"A little." He whisked his cloth over the table and put down the carafe of wine.

"Have you been to England?" I began to feel as though I were carrying out an interrogation.

"I was prisoner of war four years."

"I too. I was prisoner in Germany."

The Italian made a gesture expressing the helplessness of man in the face of international politics.

"Where were you in England?"

"Croy-don." He pronounced it in two equal syllables. "I work in factory in Croy-don. I like."

"Better than here?"

He shrugged. "All my family here. . . . Yes, I like Croy-don better. My daughter," he indicated the child, who was as fair as he was dark, "she half-English."

"You married an English girl?" Sibyl said.

He laughed. "No. My daughter born while I prisoner in Croy-don. Father English. English soldier." He didn't seem to mind it much; treated it merely as another hazard of war. He ruffled the girl's hair affectionately. "She very pretty, eh?"

"Very pretty."

He sighed, then he brightened. "I also have daughter of mine in England. Same age as this one." He grinned, as though he thought it fair exchange, and hurried off to serve a party of lorry-drivers who had just arrived.

We drove hard all that afternoon, leaving the Abruzzi far

behind, through the densely populated vineyard country of Umbria, past Lake Trasimeno with its villas and lidos, and into Tuscany. I pulled off the road at last on to a flat sandy patch of scrub oak and pine and switched off the engine. Soon Sibyl had the petrol stove roaring under the can of water, and I sat with my back against a rock, watching the bubbles begin to rise, relaxed after the long journey.

A boy had drawn near in the usual silent way and stood a few yards from the car, looking at us. He smiled but did not answer when I greeted him. He was tall for his age, I put him down as about ten or eleven, and there was something American in his long loose-limbed body and thick fair hair. I did a rapid calculation and decided that this one was too old to be a result of the Liberation. "Do you speak English?" I asked.

He smiled again and shook his head.

"He's shy," Sibyl said.

I like shy children. In fact all the people I've really liked all my life have been shy. "Perhaps he'd like a bar of chocolate," I said.

She offered the chocolate, and he smiled again but would not take it.

"Perhaps they're different up here." I had always been brought up to refuse anything from strangers. I was brought up to be diffident too. I used to blame my parents for it when I was younger, but now I'm not so sure.

Still smiling shyly and still refusing hospitality the boy watched us drink our tea. Sibyl turned to wave to him as we left the wood and he stood there, not moving, watching us out of sight. I wondered if it was a sign of middle age to think your parents might be right. But I do like shy people. Mike was basically shy and so is Sibyl, for all her poise. Children are brash today because they are being forced to grow up too soon. They are brought up to be self-confident before they have anything to be confident about. They are treated as equals in the home, they are weaned on television where they see celebrities acting the fool for their amusement, they hear members of Parliament insulting each other and discussing world politics as though it's all as simple as ABC. And then they are thrown out into the real world where they find they don't know everything, where world politics are not as simple as ABC, where the young are not necessarily more important than the old. They get a sudden shock and a lot of them go to pieces, or to a psychiatrist. It's not self-confidence they have been given after all, it's brashness. . . .

There were two policemen dressed in light summer uniform standing spaced out across the road, with rifles at the ready. As I braked I realised that they were on their toes prepared to jump to one side should I change my mind. One of the men came forward along the passenger's side of the car. The other stood back, keeping us covered.

The first one stopped suddenly and stared across Sibyl at me as though he had never seen a beard before. His comrade lowered his rifle and came up behind him.

"*Signore!*" The first policeman touched his cap, stepped back on to his comrade's toes and ran round the bonnet to the driver's side. He fumbled in the breast pocket of his creased khaki tunic and pulled out a diary and a stub pencil, both of which he thrust in my face. "*Scusi signore! Per favore!*"

Uncomprehending but willing I took the notebook and signed my name.

"*Grazie signore!*" But the disappointment on the man's face when he saw the signature was pathetic. He made a long speech the only words of which I recognised were "Ernest 'Emingway."

I grinned and shook my head. I let in the clutch and the car moved forward.

"You should have signed Ernest Hemingway you know," Sibyl said.

"I know, I'm kicking myself. I didn't realise until it was too late."

"I knew as soon as I saw their faces. Did you smell the wild flowers?"

"I thought it was the policemen. . . . I shall have to shave it off."

"Oh no, I like it! Besides think how much earlier we have breakfast now."

I had grown the beard because I hated shaving and because now, for the second time in my life, I was free to grow a beard. I had worked it out: Say twenty minutes a day for shaving—I was a slow shaver—twenty minutes a day for a shaving life of seventy years worked out at fifty-seven weeks. Over a year of shaving, night and day, without stopping to eat. The thousands of sticks of shaving soap, the blades, the brushes. The idea was fantastic.

The road to Siena lay along a hog's back above rolling fields of pink-stemmed burnished wheat, the contours smoothed by generations of tilling. Grey-green olives grew in patterns in the wheatfields and where the wheat had been cut the colour was lighter, almost white. On the thin green fallow peasants dressed in black were spreading muck in evenly spaced rich brown splashes. There were solid stone farms set on low hills, with thin double lines of black cypresses joining them to the road. Each farm had its own cluster of conical haystacks built round poles, echoing the shape of the cypresses in their hard shadow. The rock at the roadside was golden ageing to ochre, and above everything was the high soft blue sky with small white clouds floating slowly, never darkening the early evening sun.

When I stopped the car in the shell-shaped Campo in the centre of Siena the pigeons took off with a clap of wings and circled in the sun above the town. I looked up to watch their hurtling flight, and the blood-red crenellated buildings seemed to move against the sky. The hard silhouette looked unreal, like a toy fort or a cardboard cut-out with forced theatrical perspective. It was Gothic, thirteenth and fourteenth century, and the baroque fountain in the square was ornate against the clean-cut simplicity of the surrounding buildings.

It was cool inside the Palazzo Publico and less crowded than the square. We walked through the rooms and admired the mural paintings, but were glad to be out in the sun again. "We'll go and have a look at the cathedral," I suggested. "Paintings *en masse* are too much for me. If I could have one or two of them, alone, in my own room, I should enjoy them, but galleries are another matter."

"You must have time," Sibyl said. "The only way to look at pictures in a gallery is to dash in, look for a long time at one picture and dash out. And then go in another day and look at it again. It's no use wandering round looking at every one, and pressing on. All that does is make you depressed that so many people have striven to put a little truth, a little of their glimpse of life, on to a canvas—and here they are all hung up in rows in a cold, empty place. They were never meant to be shown like that."

"The Chinese have the right idea. They have a lot of paintings but only show one at a time. They keep all the others stowed away somewhere and change them over when they feel like it."

The cathedral occupied the summit of the hill on which the city stood. It was built of marble in horizontal bands of black and white and the campanile, soaring like a tower should, bore its banding proudly; but the wedding cake façade lacked the simplicity of the tower and the dramatic colour contrast fought a losing battle with the encrusting decoration.

Inside there was less carving, and the black and white bands of marble and the semi-circular arches looked Moorish and voluptuous in contrast to the angular spikiness of the exterior. Part had been roped off for the worship of God, and in this small pen a group of the devout were carrying out the ritual, oblivious of the parties of foreign tourists. I heard English, American, French, German and Italian, each guide monopolising a portion of the building and pointing out the items of interest while his charges gazed stiff-necked at the decorated ceiling, scuffled on the wooden boards which hid most of the marble pavement, or peeped furtively at the congregation. Through the open doorway I saw a girl in a yellow blouse and red skirt with a man in a bright blue jersey walk slowly across the courtyard, and I realised how the place had looked crowded with men and women in harsh heraldic colours, with contrasting hose and parti-coloured doublets.

When we came out of the cathedral the tops of the towers and roofs were caught in sunlight but here, in the deep chasms of the streets, the shadows lay heavily across the open doorways of the houses. It was not difficult to imagine Siena in medieval times. Then the loudest noise to be heard in the streets was the cry of man, the sound of horses' shoes on cobbles or the silver note of a trumpet. This town had been preserved by the Italian people as a national monument. Architecturally Siena had come to a halt in medieval times and her people lived now much as they had lived then, but in peace. I wondered what had taken the place of the wars which had necessitated these high walls and ramparts, the fight between the Guelphs and Ghibellines which had tempered the manhood of its princes and their armies. If the men of Siena no longer need to defend their town, if the Guelphs of one street no longer fight the Ghibellines in the next, what has happened to the manhood in the man? Has it gone, burned out in the fire of the city's history of belligerence? Or do they own

Lambrettas and risk their lives on the crowded weekend roads? Was that why the town was silent? Why were there no young men among those who sat on chairs outside the houses in the safety of the narrow streets which had never been defiled by the exhaust gas of a car?

CHAPTER THIRTEEN

"WE'LL JUST go and look at the pictures." I took the plate of bacon and eggs and sat down at the table. "We haven't much time, so we'll dash through like we did in Siena." I looked round me at the sun-dappled smooth brown sandy floor of the chestnut forest. "I know it's all wrong but if we've seen all of them once we shall know what to come back for to see again. I mean, it would be too silly to spend all day looking at a Tintoretto when in the next room there was a Titian we should have much preferred. Anyway, I want to see the picture that Mark Twain said was the obscenest picture ever painted."

"Which one is that?" She turned off the stove and sat down to her breakfast.

"Titian's Venus."

"Where is it?"

"In the Uffizi Gallery." I watched the sun play with a strand of hair which had fallen loose from the scarf she had tied round her head. The light slanted along the side of her face, throwing a blue shadow to the collar of the white shirt. What did I want with Titian's Venus on canvas, when I had this?

"Why did he think it so obscene?"

"He wrote about it at the end of the nineteenth century, and to an American anything to do with Europe was pretty depraved. It was Art and they had no time for Art. They had no past, therefore they would look only to the future. Fear was really at the back of it all. Mark Twain's travel books were supposed to be funny, they *are* funny in parts, but there's a lot of fear behind them all the same."

"I haven't read Mark Twain." Her eyes when she is under trees are flecked with green. Indoors they are brown, sometimes almost black.

"A generation of Americans was brought up on them, more's the pity. A generation who now thinks that everyone in Europe is depraved, dirty, backward and corrupt. Yet because of the background of fear in the books they're afraid of us, afraid of our culture."

"And it's all Mark Twain's fault." She smiled and the laughter lines came in her face.

"He may have been the voice of the people. He was a journalist before he wrote a book and made enough money to do the Grand Tour."

"Like us."

"His tour was a bit grander than ours. He pitied people travelling on their own. He went with a party and thought that the only possible way to travel was to take your own little world along with you. You had something to judge by then."

"We all do that, in our minds. The only other way is to live in a country for a long time, then you can write from the inside outwards."

"He made too much fun. He wrote for his public, I suppose, that vast public who would never go to Europe and liked to hear that things were so much better ordered at home. He was the direct cause of all this Isolation business."

"He must be turning in his grave by now."

"They're responsible for a lot, writers. Kipling, Buchan, Dornford Yates and others like them were directly responsible for a lot of the bravery and cheerfulness in the two World Wars. They may have been a bit boneheaded in their insularity but that's the attitude that wins wars, there's no getting away from it."

"I'm not so sure it's the insularity entirely. It's more than that. All the heroes of their books were sure. They had their standards and they stuck to them and so they never let the reader down. The trouble with the heroes in fiction nowadays is that they let everybody down. They don't stick to their standards, they pretend they don't have any—but they must have otherwise they wouldn't be so dissatisfied with their own behaviour. And because the heroes are heroes no longer people are turning away from fiction and finding true life ones instead. But the long-haired boys will soon crawl out of their holes and counter-attack by trying to prove that those chaps are as sordid and mean and seedy as their own creation." She grinned and her belligerence vanished. "Do you remember those two in the Brevet Club? They felt they had missed a vital experience in being still too young to fight by the end of the war. No man in his senses would wish for a war, and yet they felt they needed one to prove themselves."

I had a vivid picture of the two immaculately dark-suited

young men sitting opposite us at the small snack-bar. I had gathered from their conversation that they were junior editors in a well-known publishing house, and one of them had been complaining bitterly. 'It's not so much that I object to these chaps being war heroes', he'd said, viciously attacking his steak, 'What I can't stand is the fact that they all write books about it. Why can't they rest on their laurels instead of muscling in on the writer's province?' It had been impossible not to eavesdrop and Sibyl was listening openly, with a gleam in her eyes. Afterwards we'd all drunk beer together and the boy had said, handsomely, that it was sour grapes really. They felt the previous generation had stolen a march on them by having had that experience, and it left his own with a feeling of futility and nothing to write about.

It must do something to you, to face death twice a week for months on end. Not the possibility of death, like being in an air-raid or even walking about London in peacetime, but being cooped up in the sky in a small box with great vulnerable wings spread out on each side of you and with four engines which so easily catch fire, or fail, and send you hurtling down. Being held in a cone of searchlights and knowing that the men down there are trying to kill you, that with their radar they can tell your height and speed, and that at this very moment they are setting the fuses of high explosive shells that will be aimed at you, to blow you out of the sky. And having bombed, to sit there in the darkness, thinking that soon it will be over (except for the flak on the coast that you know will be terrific) and suddenly to hear the urgency in the rear-gunner's voice as he shouts, 'Night fighter, skipper, coming in from port!' And just sitting there, not able to do much but knowing that he's there with cannon and machine-guns, coming in to pump you full of holes, to set you on fire so that the red living flames flash back and tear the flesh in ribbons from your hands and face. To know this, week in, week out, and to come back each time to the ordinary people living ordinary lives and to learn each time you come back that one or two crews did not come back—and that next time it will be you.

Was it the thrill of danger that made the war still the most important thing in many people's lives, that made them turn to war books, plays and films? Partly, but that wasn't quite all. It was more the instinctive feeling that this man, the writer of the war book, had something to tell, something we should know. It wasn't only that he had faced death and been frightened, it was that he had been alone; that in the sky, on the sea, on the run from captivity, he had been cut off from society. For a short time he had been a hunted animal with all the animal's keen perception. Generations of civilisation had been sloughed off and the man had emerged as he was meant to be, responsible to himself. It did not happen only in the war. Men sought it in peacetime on the mountaintops, in deserts, in the air. But in war it had happened to so many.

"There are ways even in peacetime," I said, now, having had my war. "You can try to climb Everest, or cross the Atlantic in a small boat, or hunt big game. But they're so darned expensive."

"You've got to be free to do it, that's the main thing."

"It's ridiculous how guilty you feel if you are free and everyone else is still imprisoned. I felt it after I'd escaped, thinking of all the chaps still kicking their heels in Germany. Some of them had been trying to get out for much longer than I had. And I felt it again this spring, when we were out in the open air, writing the script, and wandering round Germany looking for a location—when everyone else was at work. I feel it even now. I've a feeling of guilt because I didn't go back with George."

"We were often working when other people were free, at nights, and weekends."

"Not quite the same sort of work. We liked doing it."

"I know what you mean, but what can we do about it? If you do what everyone else does, it doesn't make it one whit less dreary for those who hate it. Most people actually enjoy it, because of the companionship, and they don't necessarily want the things we want. A lot of them would regard a camping holiday with horror. If they truly hate their jobs they change them or train for something they'd like to do, or emigrate. There *is* still adventure if you're determined to have it."

"Most of them have ties and can't just uproot themselves."

"Then they've made the choice. They've decided they prefer the ties to the adventure. And they can still take part in the adventure, in books, even if only vicariously. You do far more for them by writing books it gives them pleasure to read than by sharing their daily round."

I could see where this conversation was leading now. Before I could look round I would be crossing the Pacific in a canoe, or risking my life driving a jeep to the more dangerous parts of Asia. "You get on with the washing up," I said. "I want to see Titian's Venus."

The Boboli Gardens were crowded and the gravel paths hot under our feet. Even the shrubs and trees looked parched. "It's no use," I said. "We ought to come here in the winter, and go through the galleries with a painter who could explain the pictures. The guides only tell you little snippets of gossip about the private lives of the artists, how Cellini burned all his furniture and melted all his pewter to cast the Perseus, or how Filippo Lippi slept with a couple of the nuns who were his models. They don't tell you anything about the paintings except their history."

"You can't expect them to," Sibyl said, "or they'd be teaching art."

"I suppose not. We always expect too much."

At first I had been annoyed by the attendant's insistence that we should tour the galleries in the prescribed order, first this room, then that, but later I was grateful for this insistence. Here was Italian painting set out as it had developed from the twelfth to the eighteenth century, from the purely religious to the frankly voluptuous. But once again there had been too many paintings, too many Madonnas, too many Crucifixions, too many square yards of naked flesh.

We had spent the whole morning in the Uffizi Palace and when we came out Florence was hot and stuffy. We had sat long over our lunch in an open-air café in the shaded corner of the Piazza della Signoria and from there had walked across the fourteenth-century bridge lined with jewellers' and goldsmiths' shops to the Pitti Palace. Already we had seen more than we could appreciate. I had found myself hurrying through the galleries, anxious to get it over, anxious to be out of it and in the open country.

"I'm glad we saw them all," I said. "Some of them stand out in my memory more than others. Titian's Venus not at all. I remember Botticelli's Birth of Venus and Uccello's battle pictures, and one or two of the Raphael portraits."

"I liked the collection of self-portraits," Sibyl said. "And that fresco in Siena of a sea fight, the one by Spinello Aretino—and those three little pictures that were so much like drawings by James Thurber. Do you remember, the Temptation of

Joseph, where a big hefty woman in a nightgown is dragging poor Joseph into bed?"

"It looked more like a rape than a temptation to me," I said. "What about shopping for dinner, eh? What's the next port of call?"

"Milan, to call on Mondadori. We're getting short of time so I suggest we stick to the main road: Bologna, Piacenza, Milan."

"Good—Bologna sausage for dinner. We pick up the money from Morino in Milan."

"We'll have sausage for lunch tomorrow, I've already bought the meat for dinner and it won't keep in this heat."

"We'll try to get to Milan so that I can see Mondadori before they go to lunch. I suppose I'd better get into a suit in the morning."

"It depends what you want to do," she said. "Terrify them or persuade them."

"It's all right for you to laugh. You haven't got to face them. Of course, they may not have read it yet."

"I'm afraid they will have. You'd better wear it. One should look one's best to see one's publisher."

"He's not my publisher yet."

"No. But he's going to be."

I wondered. It was a delicate subject to bring up. If he spoke perfect English I could explain it well enough. In war one despised the enemy, otherwise the whole thing became pointless, and as a prisoner derision was one's only weapon. When I had written the book I had tried, in re-creating the atmosphere of the prison camp, to re-create the dialogue of the prisoners, and to us the Italians had been Wops. Now when I was asking this great publishing house to translate the book into the Italian language, I must explain this passage. I must offer to re-write it so as not to destroy the scene but to bring the dialogue into line with what I now knew of the Italian people. No, that's not true, I thought. You don't know them any better now than you did then. That's not what you mean at all. You mean you want to re-write it so as not to prejudice the Italian reading public. If what you wrote about the prisoners then was honest, it's honest about them now. I remembered the room full of English aircrew herded together in the German prison camp. Probably not one of them had ever seen an Italian on the soil of Italy. Probably not one of them had ever met an Italian at home in England. Most of them had gone to war without ever having met a German. Because we were at war we called the Italians Wops and the Germans Goons. I could easily omit that passage from the book. It would be stupid to antagonise Italian readers because of a few words of dialogue and, after all, you wrote a book to sell it. I thought of my English publisher and how he carefully checked every manuscript with 'our American end' in mind.

But that was only part of it. Already since the book was published there were parts I would re-write, and I should go on probably all my life wanting to re-write more and more. Otherwise there would be no progress. What was honest then was not necessarily honest now.

It would not be so easy, I thought, to explain all this to Mondadori.

CHAPTER FOURTEEN

THE POLICEMAN stopped all lanes of traffic and got down from his pedestal. He crossed the road, and touched his cap with a white-gloved hand. "Sir, you may not park here."

"I'm sorry. I've arranged to meet my wife. If I move she will not know where to look for me. She will not be long."

"OK." He apparently realised the hopelessness of it all. He saluted again and returned to the traffic chaos which had built up in his absence.

I sat in the car, trying not to inhale the exhaust smoke, hoping that Sibyl would not be late, conscious that I was the cause of much of the horn-blowing which was making the air of Milan hideous at that moment. Then she appeared with her big raffia basket, walking slowly out of the entrance to the Gallery, looking at her watch. She knew me and ran the last few yards. "I missed you," she said. "What happened, are they going to do it?"

"Get in," I said. "That policeman will lose his job if we don't move from here. Come and navigate me out of this city, quickly."

"Not until you tell me."

"Yes of course they are. Now hurry."

"What were they like?" She put the laden basket behind her seat and climbed in over the door.

"You concentrate on your job. I'll tell you everything when we're up on the Autostrada." We had fitted the compass to the dashboard for this purpose. In the centre of a foreign city, not speaking the language, the best thing was to find your own way; and if you hadn't got a detailed map of the city the best way of doing that was with a compass. Sibyl orientated herself and began to navigate me through the hurtling traffic.

"If only all the streets went east and west," she said.

"Which way now?"

"Next on the left—no, that's a one-way street—try the next one."

"What?"

"Left—left!"

I turned sharply, and before I was a couple of yards down the street a thousand Milanese pointed out vociferously that this too was one way. I swore and reversed out, the back of the car feeling very vulnerable as I exposed it to the stream of traffic. I took the next on the left into a short street with a large stone building across the end.

"Turn right at the bottom."

But the right turn was only an alley and we were stopped dead by a large pantechnicon unloading at a warehouse. I tried to edge past, hoping the enthusiastic porters with the heavy cupboard would respect the cellulose, avoiding by inches a small man buried under a pile of cane chairs, until I was brought finally to a standstill by meeting another car head-on. The driver, smiling broadly, opened his door and leaned out. "You are going the wrong way."

"Which way is the Autostrada?"

"It is difficult from here. So many streets are for one direction only. Follow me, I will guide you there."

I backed out past the pantechnicon to allow the car, a small open Fiat with a sun awning striped like a Venetian blind, to go through. The man obviously knew his way about Milan, and his car was half the width of the Bentley. For the next few miles I concentrated entirely on the Venetian blind as it darted in and out among the fast-moving traffic, until at last it drew into the kerb in a broad boulevard.

The man was out of the Fiat before I had braked, and I had to scramble out quickly in order to acknowledge such kindness on my feet. "You go straight ahead now," he said. "You cannot miss the Autostrada."

"It is very kind of you to take so much trouble."

"It is nothing. I hope you have a good journey."

I looked sideways at Sibyl as we drove away. "He got us out of a pretty mess."

"It was all those one-way streets. Now if I had a good map . . ."

"A compass is one way of navigating," I said. "Another is to find a man who speaks perfect English, has a car, and knows his city like the back of his hand."

The entrance to the Autostrada was in Totalitarian style and might have been the entrance to a football stadium. There were a number of ticket kiosks in chipped concrete, and I drew in behind a brand new streamlined Lancia, then seeing that another kiosk would be quicker pulled out and changed lanes.

"When are they going to publish it?"

"They didn't say. They've got to get it translated first of course."

"I hope they get someone good."

I laughed. "That's exactly what I said. Apparently they have a saying in Italy, *Traduttore—traditore!*"

"What's that mean?"

"Translator—traitor."

There was a snarl of exhaust and the Lancia rocketed past, tyres squealing on the concrete. The two men in the front seat stared straight ahead.

"We can't let them get away with that," she said.

"Shall I beat them up?" The road was as good as a race track. I do not often drive her flat out, but this was an occasion. I edged my seat forward and pressed on the accelerator.

"Did you see Mondadori himself?"

"Good lord no. That would have been like asking to see God." The Lancia was two cars ahead and going fast. "I saw one of the editors. Quite a nice chap. He'd read the book."

"Was it all right about the Wops?"

"He couldn't have been more charming."

When we passed the Lancia the two young men in well-cut business suits did not look, so I opened the silencer cut-out and gave them a blast of the straight-through exhaust.

"What are they doing now?" She never looked round, for fear of seeming to crow.

"They're coming up," I said, looking in the mirror. I trod harder on the accelerator and watched the rev counter.

"What sort of place was it?"

"Oh, typical publisher's. Palatial. Panelled corridors dripping with oil paintings, crimson carpets, a waiting-room like a ducal library. And a sacrosanct air about it all." I could see the Lancia in the driving mirror. It had pulled out and was trying to come past. I edged in to the near kerb to give them plenty of room, but stood hard on the accelerator and slowly drew away. "You know, publishers, booksellers and authors always accuse the other two of making the money out of books. But you've only got to compare the three standards of living, to see who does."

The Lancia was coming up on our quarter and there were two slow cars in front. We were approaching a rise in the road. I lifted my foot from the accelerator, then trod hard on the brake and felt her dig herself in. The Lancia shot forward and scraped through in front of a big blue coach coming in the opposite direction.

"Blimey," she said. "That was lucky. What was the editor's office like?"

"A bit more spartan, but he'd a nice collection of sculptor's drawings."

"Who by?"

"It took me all my time to find out the important things.... They produced a photographer on the spot, and the publicity manager interrogated me."

"They seem well organised."

"I think we've got the best people. Thanks to Peter Moore." We were up with the Lancia again and the road was open and wide in front of us. I put my foot down hard and watched the needle of the rev counter approach the red mark on the dial. The Lancia seemed to be labouring as we passed, and the driver and his passenger were smiling.

"Sounds a bit tinny," Sibyl said. "Did they say anything about an advance?"

"Seventy-five quid. It will be in a standard library edition of foreign authors. People like Virginia Woolf and D. H. Lawrence.... But he warned me not to expect to make much more than the advance out of an Italian edition."

"Well, seventy-five pounds isn't to be sneezed at. And think of the prestige."

"We shan't get fat on prestige." We were well ahead of the Lancia now, the engine running smoothly, the wind snatching the words from my mouth, tugging at my hair. The Bentley had been built for this, would stand any amount of it, but I eased my foot slightly on the accelerator pedal and relaxed. I knew we had the faster car.

When the Lancia came past the driver and his passenger both waved. I wondered whether their car would still be on the road in sixteen years' time. "Did you see many paintings?" I said.

"Not many. It took me so long to get the food. I did see

Mantegna's *Dead Christ*. It might have been painted by Stanley Spencer, it reminded me of his *Christ In The Wilderness* series. . . . You know, he's one of the few modern painters who have the humility to paint with care. He paints with love, and so many of them have no love. Except for themselves. They're subjective, they don't try to paint like everyone else so far has painted—feeling, seeing, loving the shape, the weight, the texture, the very being of the thing they paint. They don't say, Now see this chair, the way it stands, the hardness of its wood, the way it balances, the roughness of its rush seat, its colour, the way loving hands have shaped its back. They say, This chair (looking at their canvas), this chair, what does it do to me? How do I feel about this chair? How do I feel about chairs in general? Chairs remind me of bicycles. I'll draw a bicycle."

"Did you go to the Post Office?"

"Oh yes. I forgot. There are two letters from Morino."

"We'll read them when we stop." The Lancia, still ahead, turned off the Autostrada at Bergamo and the two men smiled and in spite of their cramped position in the low-built car managed to bow and raise their hats.

"I like a good loser," Sibyl said.

"They didn't lose, they were in front."

"They'd have lost if they hadn't turned off."

I remembered the traffic queue outside Manchester, led by a slow heavy lorry. In the front of that the road was clear. The half-dozen drivers ahead of us were following the lorry obediently, each two yards behind the one in front. I was passing the third when I noticed that the driver, furious, was winding down his window. 'What's the matter with you?' the man had shouted, 'Aren't you content to keep your place in the queue?' 'No!' Sibyl had replied, and had smiled at him. Looking in the driving mirror before I turned the next corner out of sight, I had seen that although the road was still clear none of the cars had passed the lorry.

The man outside Manchester had at least kept his disapproval on a verbal plane. There were men and women, otherwise quite decent people, who would suddenly pull out to stop you overtaking them. Sometimes it amounted to attempted murder. They didn't do it because they wanted to be in front, or they said they didn't. They did it, these self-appointed policemen, because you were travelling faster than they thought you should. Surely they could see that if you came up behind them you were travelling faster than they were and they could have the courtesy to let you through?

It was the ant mind again, a growing instinct that everything not average was bad. A column of ants progresses in steady unison. There is no individual advantage to be gained by one ant overtaking another. There are no individuals. The one mass mind has but a single objective and thinks for all. The car driver outside Manchester probably had no personal dislike of being overtaken. There was this new instinct working in him that told him it was wrong. The battle between the old individual mind and the growing instinct is filling our mental hospitals, and we shall not be happy until one or the other is defeated.

"Look at those hoardings," Sibyl said. "They certainly catch the eye."

"I've been trying not to. But as a business man I must say they're efficient. Being a cussed sort of chap I'd go out of my way to avoid that particular brand of oil."

They were three-dimensional, over twenty feet high; giant replicas of an oil canister in full colour, supported by a giant hand in two dimensions. The texture of the skin of the hand, the well-manicured nails and clean shirtcuff somehow epitomised the antiseptic smugness of conformity. The whole towering edifice was secured by wire guy ropes attached to iron posts. Behind them the Alps, lovely in the evening sun, looked artificial; a painted backdrop to a Brobdingnagian puppet show.

Lake Garda was nearly three hundred miles from our camp in the Futa Pass and Milan had taken several hours of a tiring day. For the last few miles I had been indulging in my favourite image, the clear blue water and the lonely shore. It would be fun to swim in fresh water with the breathing tube and goggles.

"The west side looks better." Sibyl had been studying the map. "There are high mountains on that side and the road seems to run along the shore." But the map had not shown the villas, the hotels and bathing stations.

It was worse than the Riviera. Coming towards us down the esplanade was a small cream car with blue wheels, driven by a chauffeur in matching blue. Head and shoulders above the sliding roof was a tall pale man wearing a band-leader's jacket in shantung, and dark glasses. He held a long scarlet patent-leather leash which was attached to the collar of a magnificent cream Alsatian dog. The chauffeur was driving at about ten miles an hour, the dog trotted on the pavement, and its owner, who was using his free hand to smoke a cigarette through a long ivory holder, watched his dog take its exercise.

"I've seen it all now," Sibyl said. "I really have."

We stopped in Gardone for water, and a crowd of youths sitting in the upper windows of the house above the pump laughed and pointed at the car, shouting remarks which I could not understand. Something in their voices reminded me of the four fishermen in the early morning in the French Alps and, thrusting out my beard, I bellowed up at them in my deepest voice, "*Eh, Pablo! Pablo! Ou est mon anorak?*" The effect was startling. One boy promptly disappeared like a Jack-in-the-box, and the derisive laughter of the rest became conciliatory.

There was a notice by the pump advertising a Lido on the shore of the lake with a camping site. "What about trying that?"

"Don't you think it will be better once we get out of this town?" Sibyl does not give up so easily.

"It all looks pretty built up to me. I would like to swim. Shall we just go and look at it?"

The Lugo-Lago Lido was a rectangle of beaten earth, its entrance through an ornate wooden archway from which the paint was already peeling. The compound was protected by barbed wire and guarded by a man who sat in a rustic sentry-box at the gate. He demanded a hundred lire per person and our passports, which he inspected closely and placed in a cupboard on the wall behind him. "No!" I said, and held out my hand.

"*Si, si!*" The man demonstrated that there were several other passports in the cupboard.

"I don't care, you're not keeping these."

He protested again, but I leaned across him and took them out of the cupboard. The growth of a police state is easy and almost imperceptible.

I drove as far as possible from the other tents and began to unpack, knowing that Sibyl did not like the place. One night behind barbed wire wouldn't do her any harm, I thought.

Blast the man for thinking I would give up the passports. Probably a trick to extort more money in the morning.

I was startled by a loud clanging sound like a dozen tin cans filled with pebbles being jangled on a string. I looked towards the noise, which came from a field fenced in to a height of ten feet or more with fishnet like a giant fruit cage. The clanging was repeated, and I saw several tin cans jump into the air as though shot up by a kick. I took it to be a burglar alarm, to give warning of campers stealing the fruit, and thought how bloody silly. Then I noticed that there were no fruit bushes and saw the hides built of straw and the birds in cages.

I walked over and stood looking through the wire. There were sparrows, thrushes and larks apparently loose in the middle of the field, eating grain which had been scattered there. The whole field had been divided into narrow pens, each sealed off from its neighbour by fishnet hung from wires. The birds on the ground suddenly sprang into the air, and I saw that each one was tethered by a length of string fastened to its wings. This was attached to another, stronger string which ran the entire width of the field. Again the birds were jerked, ludicrously, painfully, spreading their wings in panic as they fell. A net flew across the top of one of the pens, forming a lid to the trap, held there by tins weighted by stones. It was this noise that had startled me.

A big fleshy man crawled out from one of the hides to make some adjustments of the system of ropes and pulleys which flicked the nets across the tops of the pens. He crawled back into his hide, and the performance was repeated. Then Sibyl was standing by my side. "What is it?"

"A trap for birds. They're only testing it."

She stood still for a moment. "Let's go somewhere else."

We packed the car and drove out under the wooden archway. The concierge ran from his sentry-box and screamed at us.

"We'll go on driving north," I said. "We'll find somewhere farther up the lake to camp."

"How was the string fixed to them?"

"Stuck with glue I expect. The ones in cages probably had their eyes put out to make them sing."

"How beastly."

"The whole business of trapping wild birds is beastly. It's

confined by law to certain times of the year, but it's a rotten business."

"Why do they sing when they've had their eyes put out? I thought they sang for joy."

"They mostly sing as a warning, to keep other birds out of their territory, I believe. Or as a danger signal or a mating call. I think it's only human sentimentality that puts it down to such a useless emotion as joy. Actually the burning of the eye damages a nerve somewhere and they just can't stop singing. They don't live for very long."

Looking all the time for a place to camp and perhaps to swim, I wondered why exactly I'd been so shocked. Logically I had no leg to stand on. I enjoyed shooting and will sit for hours in the mud of the saltings waiting for the duck to flight, or spend a whole day walking up partridge across the open fields. It was something to do with the using of decoys. I have never shot over a decoy and never want to. Yes, it was the decoy birds that sickened me, and also the use to which the captured birds were put. Kept in wicker cages in the slums of Naples, hanging in windows so that the wretched human would in his captivity have some illusion, some reminder in this captive bird of his own lost heritage of freedom.

The road now ran along a cornice about twenty feet above the water. Sometimes it tunnelled through the rock, or hung precariously buttressed to the face of sheer cliff. It was beautiful, and exhilarating to drive along, but impossible for camping. Wherever it dipped to water level there was a village, or groves of orange and lemon trees heavily fenced with wire netting. There were stalls at the roadside loaded with bunches of oranges tied together with leaves, as though they were still on the branch. We stopped and bought a bunch, but the fruit was dry and fibrous.

Then we had reached the northern extremity of the lake. "What about going down the eastern side a little way?" I suggested. "It looks better over there."

"I'm sorry about the Lido."

"That's OK, I didn't like it either." I had got my second wind. "But I don't want to leave the lake without swimming in it."

We found a narrow rocky field sheltered from view by trees and huge lichened boulders. The road here ran through a tunnel in the side of the hill and, in curving to take the mass of rock at a right-angle, left the edge of the lake. There was a stony track running down to the shore, where we parked the car out of sight of the road. We swam naked and dived off a high rock into the clear deep water, then dried ourselves and lay on the short dry grass by the water's edge in the still warm evening sun. "This is one of the best camps we've ever made," Sibyl said.

"What about those letters from Morino?"

"I'll get them."

"Read them in the right order."

She flung herself face down on her towel, and translated:

"*Monsieur, I have just received your letter and am truly pained to see that you suspect me of complicity with my husband. I have told you the whole truth and have exposed to you my plain situation just as it is, unfortunately for me and my children. I am not, and do not want to be, responsible for the faults committed by him. I do want one last time to make amends and I send you two thousand francs that the kindness of a friend who interests himself in me has been good enough to give me. I do want to say to you also that I will not stop there and as soon as I can I will send to you something more. As for the Livret de Mariage, please have the extreme kindness to send it to me because it is as much my property as that of my husband and I repeat to you that I have* absolute need *of it for my affairs. In the hope that you will be kind enough to understand and to trust me, please accept monsieur the assurances of my very distinguished sentiments, Marie Morino.*"

"I don't believe it," I said. "It's too smooth."

"She may be genuine."

"She didn't enclose the money," I pointed out. "What's in the other letter?"

The first thing to come out of the second envelope was a wad of thousand-franc notes. I counted them quickly. There were five.

"She's sent it—all of it!" Sibyl said.

"Read what she says."

"*Monsieur, You must be in possession of my letter in which I announced to you the sending of an order of two thousand francs. I now have pleasure in making good my promise of the full amount you ask of me. I remind you again that I do really need my Livret de Mariage. Please believe monsieur with my thanks the assurance of my distinguished sentiments, Marie Morino.*"

"Well I'm damned." I could still hardly believe it. "He knew when the game was up all right."

"I'm not so sure." Sibyl was looking worried. "I think she may be telling the truth. She's hardly likely to have made up that bit about the friend who interests himself in her. It makes me wonder what she's done to get the money."

"What do you want to do?"

"Send it back with the Livret."

The sweets of victory were a little sour in my mouth too, but I was determined not to be hoodwinked by the man again. "It's only about five quid, and after all he did get the coffee beans." I could not rid myself of the vision of him standing over her, dictating the letters as I had dictated mine to Sibyl. "We'll talk about it in the morning." I put the Livret and the money in the hip pocket of my trousers. "How many lire have you got left? I'll change them into Austrian money at the border."

She emptied her handbag on to the grass and we counted out the soiled currency notes.

"Just under ten thousand lire." I made a bundle of them and buttoned it into my pocket with the Livret and the francs. "We gauged that pretty well really. If I change it into schillings we should get through Austria without having to cash a traveller's cheque. We've enough petrol coupons left to top up before we cross. . . . Aren't you hungry yet?"

"I can take a hint," she said, and began to get dressed.

CHAPTER FIFTEEN

I HAD slept at first, but awoke soon after and lay for a long time on the canvas bed unable to sleep again, troubled by the thought of Madame Morino and her children. I imagined them at yearly intervals, each one representing a year of suffering. Like little steps, my mother had said, referring to the family of a neighbour, and the phrase had stuck, to be docketed and linked in some way with stepchildren so that for ever afterwards the words were to bring to mind a group of barefooted unwanted children in ascending heights, hungry and uncared-for. Supposing she were genuine, with an absent husband and the children to bring up.

Later I dozed uneasily, but kept waking suddenly as though someone had touched me on the arm. The moon had risen, flooding the tent with light. Once I crawled out under the mosquito net and stood by the edge of the lake, watching the moon on the water. The night was calm and the high cloudless sky was almost blue.

Back in the tent I turned restlessly on my bed. We'd been so lucky. I thought of Sibyl sleeping silently, like a child, a foot away. So very lucky. We'd send the five thousand francs back with the Livret as a gesture. If it were a confidence trick and he expected it, there would be just one more sucker to his credit, but at least I would not have the woman on my conscience. I fell asleep.

When I awoke it was daylight. I stretched out my hand for the drill trousers and shirt which I had left folded near my head, but there was nothing but the bare cold mackintosh groundsheet. I sat up and looked round the tent. Sibyl was asleep, but there was not a stitch of clothing anywhere, nor the camera which I had slipped under my folded trousers the night before. Even the travelling clock had gone. I shook her by the shoulder. "Come on, don't mess about! Where are my clothes?"

Her surprise as she awoke was unfeigned. "I haven't touched them. You must have put them under your pillow."

I made a cursory search but knew that I would not find them. "They're all gone."

"They can't be gone." She raised herself on the bed and looked underneath, her hair falling down like a curtain in front of her face. "They're not here." The words came indistinctly.

"We undressed in the tent," I said. Wrapping my sheet round me as a cloak I crawled outside. The surface of the lake glittered in the sun, but the air was cold. The Bentley stood where we had left her. In a neat pile behind the tent were our clothes.

"That was a damn' silly thing to do, for a start. Someone might have stolen them." But I knew as I said it that she had not put them there.

"What was? What's happened?"

"We've been robbed. He must have got his hand under the tent behind us and dragged them out." I picked up the trousers and put my hand in the hip pocket. "Madame Morino's not getting her five thousand francs. She's not even getting the Livret back."

"Where's the camera?"

"Gone. That's the unkindest cut of all."

"We'd better look at the car."

We dressed hurriedly and roughly checked the contents of the car, but nothing more seemed to be missing. I thought that probably I'd disturbed him when I'd got up in the night. If so, he'd been crouching there while I'd been standing looking at the lake. I wondered if he'd been armed. "You get breakfast. I'll have a look round."

"I walked down the rocky track towards the road, trying to reconstruct the man's approach. To be able to see through the mosquito net he would have to get between the tent and the edge of the lake. He probably crept round the boulders and returned the same way. I searched the dry stony surface but there was nothing there, and all the time I was searching I was sick with remorse at the loss of the Livret de Mariage. By now I was convinced that the woman was genuine and here we were, after holding her to ransome, unable to complete the bargain. I could cash a traveller's cheque and send her the money in Italian currency; but talk about the biter bit. The loss of the camera was sickening, but even that was less important than the Livret.

I quartered the road, through the tunnel in the hillside and out into the sun again. There, on a small patch of open ground between the road and the water's edge, neatly piled on a stone to make them conspicuous, were the Livret de Mariage and a box of French matches which had been in the side pocket of my trousers. I made a quick search of the ground and the rocks along the shore, but could find nothing else.

Walking back through the tunnel I felt ridiculously relieved to have the Livret again. Now the loss of the camera was the important thing.

"He must have thought that was our passport," Sibyl said. "He thought that we couldn't get on without it so he left it there for us to find."

"Very kind of him too. More likely thought it too incriminating to keep. Same with the matches. Being French they'd be noticed. But I had an idea while I was in the tunnel. Let's go to every village in the neighbourhood, find the camera shop and ask if they've got a Retina for sale."

"He'd hardly have sold it yet, would he?"

"It's worth trying."

"I wonder where he came from?"

"A waiter at one of the hotels, probably."

"He must have watched us undressing, to see where we put the clothes. He must have been watching us all evening."

"I expect he was."

"Oh hell!" She laughed. "Well, he got his money's worth."

"We'll go to the police," I said.

"What will they do?"

"Well, we can't let him get away with it."

"Lucille should be here to hear that."

"That was different," I said. "We'd got the stuff back then. We know the number of the camera and they should be able to trace it easily."

We ate breakfast quickly and as we should be crossing into Austria later in the day I packed carefully with the Customs in mind. We tidied up the camping site, burned the rubbish, scouted round to make sure we had left nothing behind; and I pressed the starter button.

Nothing happened.

Ever since I'd had the car she'd never failed to start at the first touch of the button. I could sometimes start her by smartly retarding the ignition lever without using the starter motor at all, a trick they had taught me at the Bentley Works. I pressed the starter again. Nothing happened; and I was conscious of the pathos of that heavy mass of complicated machinery when its life blood of current is cut off.

"Is it the battery?" Sibyl said. "It's pretty old."

"No, the battery's all right. Get out and give her a push. It's downhill."

She got out, and pushed. As the car moved forward I let in the clutch in second gear, and the engine started.

In the village at the end of the lake a boy who spoke good English guided us to the police station, riding in front of the car on his bicycle, and when I found that the brigadier spoke no English I fetched him in to act as interpreter.

"He wants to know your name and where you come from," the boy said. "And the name of your wife and of your children."

I gave my name and the policeman, who was smoking a thin cigar, wrote it in his book.

"He wants the other names," the boy said. "And also that of your father."

"Tell him they're immaterial."

"Please?"

"Tell him they are of no importance."

The policeman replied briefly in Italian, without removing his cigar.

"He says that he must know this for his record."

"Tell him that I've come here to report a theft, not to request nationalisation."

The boy told it to the policeman, and this time he replied at some length, with much repetition and emphasis and flourishing of the cigar, which miraculously held its ash.

"He says that it is necessary for him to have the particulars of the person who is making the complaint."

"Tell him that this complaint has nothing to do with my father, who is dead. Tell him that I've changed my mind." I turned to leave the office but the policeman, who was agile for a man of his size, barred the way.

"He wishes to see your passport," the boy said.

I showed the man my passport and the documents for the car; I supposed he had a right to ask for these.

"He says you must report here tomorrow," the boy said.

"Tell him I shall be in Austria tomorrow. Tell him to—oh, never mind. Tell him the thief was five foot eleven, with a bald head, a drooping moustache, and a pot belly." The description exactly fitted the brigadier.

I was still fuming with indignation when I joined Sibyl and the dignity of our departure was marred by the fact that the car again failed to start. Acutely conscious of the policeman watching from behind lace curtains I pushed, with Sibyl in the driving seat. I could almost hear him thinking, One of those effete bastards who let their women drive. "They needn't think they're getting away with it," I panted. "We'll do the camera shops."

But after a weary morning trying to make myself understood in four shops in four different lakeside villages and pushing the car to get it started, I realised that it was hopeless. "We'll never get it back," I said. "The only thing to do in this country is either sleep with everything of value under your pillow, or tie it in something and suspend it from the top of the tent."

"Can't we fix the sides of the tent down to the ground in some way so that it's impossible to get a hand underneath?"

"I could pull the groundsheet up and tie it to the brailing. I'll do that tonight. At least our heads will be protected."

"Every time I think of it I feel sick."

"Would you like to stay in an hotel tonight?" I suggested. "It'll be getting cold from now on, as we drive north."

"Oh no!" She was firm about that. "We've only three more nights. We can't be put off by a little thing like this."

"I'll take the axe into the tent with me. Although I hardly think the same thing would happen two nights running."

"Touch wood," she said.

We stopped in Bolzano to exchange our last petrol coupons. This was an Alpine town, and there was a tang in the air. Street names, traffic signs and notices in shop windows were in two languages, and most of the people in the streets were speaking German.

"Look," I said, "if they speak German here I'll cash enough cheques to take her to a garage. I reckon I can make myself understood."

"But will they understand the car?"

"We'll find that out first. I'll go into it very carefully with them and I won't let them touch her unless I'm sure they're competent." When I had bought the car I'd taken her to the

Works and asked them for a test and an estimate for the replacement of any worn or faulty parts. Without turning a hair a dark, competent-looking tester had left the six-thousand-pound Rolls on which he had been working, donned an old leather motoring coat and driven off in my sixteen-year-old open tourer. I had waited with majestic white-haired Mr Clarke, proud veteran of the old Bentley racing days. "Don't worry," he said, "if he comes back and says that everything is wrong. You can discount what he says by half. He's our most particular man and he'll put her through her tricks." An hour later the tester had come back. "There's a faint chatter in the rocker gear I don't like. But we'll put that right in half a day. Apart from that she's perfect." Clarke had grinned like a boy. "Knew she would be. A little lady, that car." "Have you had it in before?" I said. "Course we have. B1AE. She's the first we made. I could turn up the record and tell you every repair that's been done on her. And that's not much." Before we'd left for France I had taken her in for tuning, and Mr Clarke had drawn me to one side. "Just give her the three liquids," he had said. "Petrol. Oil. And water. Apart from that, don't touch her. Remember that. Don't touch her. She won't go wrong."

I chose the biggest garage in Bolzano and regretted it the moment I saw the foreman in a white house-surgeon's overall. I have an aversion to non-working foremen in clean overalls, knowing from experience it means inefficiency and a grossly inflated bill. "Do you speak English?" I asked.

The foreman smiled and shook his head.

"*Deutsch?*"

"*Jawohl.*"

"*Elektrik,*" I said. "*Spezialist, Elektrik.*"

"*Moment, bitte.*" He walked away and returned some minutes later with another man in blue overalls and thick-lensed spectacles.

"Good morning sir." It was the man in the blue overalls.

I reverted thankfully to English. "There is something wrong with my self-starter."

"We are very busy," the specialist said. "If it is not serious, we can put it right." The fact that they were very busy had not prevented the gathering of most of the mechanics who were asking Sibyl the age, mark and speed of this extraordinary car.

He dismissed this evidence with an impatient wave of his hand. "It is the battery. Please show me where is the battery."

The battery is under the floorboards in the back of the car. Reluctantly, now not so sure that I had been right about the man, I unloaded the gear piece by piece and handed it to Sibyl to stack in a neat pile on the path outside the house; the tent, bedroll, water jars, suitcase, crate of food, and finally, the guns. "We are camping," Sibyl said, in unnecessary explanation.

"We too camp," Frau Schiller said. "Sometimes we leave the children, and my man and I go up into the mountains and camp, and we are young again."

I took up the floorboards. The terminals of the battery were corroded and with a grunt of satisfaction Willi seized one of them. It came away in his hand. I turned to Sibyl. "It's not the hitting."

"No," she said. "It's knowing how hard to hit."

"It is a good car," Willi said. "We knew this mark before the war, as racing car." He examined the dashboard and saw the compass. He stood upright and looked at me. "You are airman?"

"I was, in the war. The compass is useful in cities. There's no way of navigating once you get among the buildings if you can't see the sun."

"I too, in the war. I fly Me.110."

"I was in bombers."

"In North Africa?"

"No," I said. "I was based in England."

"I was in Munich when the British bombed," Frau Schiller said. "It was terrible. Women and children killed."

Her husband was fitting the new terminals on the battery. The way that he tightened the nuts on the soft metal studs reminded me of Ted, the mechanic in our local garage. You can always tell, as soon as a man takes up a spanner, what sort of a mechanic he is. There is a tender strength in the way Ted tightens a nut, and this man was the same.

"War is war," Willi said. "It was better in Africa. There were no civilians, just armies. I did not enjoy the war so much when we were moved back into Germany." He straightened himself from where he was bending over the battery. "And now I am here. At first after the war I am in Munich, but there I am not happy. I am worker in factory and am nothing. It is stupid to live in city and earn more money but not be happy. Here in village I do not earn much money, and I work more. But we are free. Here I am Auto-Elektrik Spezialist. Here, in the winter I ski, in the summer I climb. It is beautiful here and I enjoy my work because I work for myself."

I replaced the floorboards over the battery and began to reload the car. "Will you go back into the Air Force if Germany rearms?"

For a moment he looked haunted. "I would like . . ." He glanced at his wife, and shook his head. "No. It is not possible. I am too old. I have a good life here. No, I stay in Austria."

I fastened down the tonneau cover. "How much do I owe you?"

"It is nothing. I do it for another airman."

"The war is over," I said. "It is business now. You must make me a proper charge." I did not want to accept charity. The fellow airman line, although it was not meant like that, reminded me of the interrogator at *Dulag-Luft* when he had wanted to shake my hand and talk as one airman to another, to extract information.

"I will charge you for the new terminals," Willi said, "and nothing for the time."

"Thank you. But perhaps your wife would like some coffee." I unfastened the cover again and took one of the tins of ground coffee out of the floorwell.

Frau Schiller clasped the tin tightly in both hands as though she feared to drop it. "There is no coffee here," Willi said. "Nor in Germany. You would do better to sell it on the black market there than to give it away." He laughed. "The last British who came to me were students. They had an old car. They said it was a London-taxi. The electrics were *kaput*. I spend two days and put it in good order. My wife cook their food, and they sleep in the taxi. When they go, they say they cannot pay, they are students. It would be better if they tell me first. I would help them, yes, but I would not do so much."

We turned off the main road, past a *Gasthaus* and over a stout wooden bridge spanning a fast-running stream, on to a bumpy track which ran back along the bank into the forest. I reversed on to a small green clearing which was in full sunshine, on the mountain side of the track. Behind us the fir forest stretched darkly upwards, thinning as it reached the peak.

I hung a line for Sibyl in the sun, between a larch and the windscreen, and while she washed the clothes I fetched buckets of water and swilled down the car. When it was dry we polished the cellulose until it shone brilliantly. Then we bathed, laughing with excitement as we splashed in the icy stream, slipping on the rocks which were smooth and oval, speckled like giant sparrows' eggs. Several times in the afternoon we were passed by peasants going up or down the rutted track, and towards evening we heard the slow hollow clonk-clonk of bells as a young boy drove a herd of heavy cattle from a pasture higher up the mountain. The cows, sweet-smelling and clean, swayed soft-footed through and round the encampment and the boy threw stones and called them by name, to keep them on the move. We wished him "*Grüss Gott*" and he stopped to talk, in a mixture of English and German. There were many roe-deer in the forest, he told us, and at night the deer would come down from the timber to feed in the higher pastures. "They come every night," he said. "I come sometimes to listen."

When the boy had followed his cows into the yard behind the Gasthaus by the bridge we ate dinner, dressed now in warm slacks and sweaters in the keen evening air. "Do you think we should take the guns into the tent tonight?" Sibyl said.

"What for, to use? Or in case they're stolen?"

"Well both. I should think the sight of a shotgun would scare most people off."

"Might be a good idea. The only snag is that this is bound to be a game reserve. If the forester came along and found us with a couple of guns in the tent he'd probably haul us in. I don't know which would be worse."

"We'll leave them in the car."

We had finished our meal when the boy came back, wearing a green ski-cap and a cloak of soft green loden. "I come to take you to listen to the roe-deer," he said.

Sibyl looked at me. "What about the gear?"

"It'll be all right. No one can steal the car." I had fitted a secret ignition switch, to discourage garage hands who wanted to hear how the engine sounded. I grinned. "You can stay and keep guard if you like."

"What—and miss the roe?"

"Come on," I said. "We mustn't be governed by our

possessions, or life will become unbearable. If they steal, they steal. There's only one thing I can't replace and I'm taking that along with me." I did not think that they would steal. Like the mountain peasants in Italy, the men and women who had passed to and from their work in the fields above had not begged with prying eyes but had greeted us courteously from the path, going about their business with dignity, respecting privacy. It did not seem logical that the boy would take us to listen to deer in the darkness of an Alpine forest as a cloak to petty thieving.

He led us up the track to the edge of a small paddock fenced with rough-hewn planks, and settled himself down at the foot of the fence where his raised head would be hidden by one of the uprights. I chose my place a few yards away, and sank into the springy heather growing between the fence and the forest which stretched brown-floored and already dark behind us. Sibyl crouched in the shadow of the next post, beyond me. There was still some daylight here, and across the paddock I could see the silver wood of the fence outlined against the blackness of the forest. "There is a break in the fence." The boy pointed it out. "There they will come. Listen."

I became aware of the water tumbling over stones in the distance. Otherwise there was silence. The forest seemed devoid of life, dark, impenetrable; straight trunks vanishing into the blackness of the foliage. Where a fallen tree had allowed the sun to penetrate there was heather, lank grass and brambles, but elsewhere the floor was a clean carpet of brown needles.

The boy stirred and I strained my eyes but could see nothing. Now he was quivering like a dog, pointing with his head. There was a sharp deep sound between a bark and a snort and, peering through the near-darkness, I could distinguish several shadowy shapes, patches of darker shadow which moved forward, paused, and moved again. Once more I heard the coughing bark sharp and clear across the width of the field, but the moving shadows had merged again into the background of the trees.

We stayed for some time longer, but the deer had gone. I relaxed and turned to look at the boy, tense, enthralled; and I wondered what urban civilisation had to offer in exchange for this. The street corner, the cinema? The dance hall? This boy would know the deer, know them from the newly dropped fawn staggering on spindle legs in early summer to the adult

ski-ing, and to re-visit some of the places I had known as a prisoner. *Dulag-Luft* was then being used by the Allies for the same purpose, and I had asked to see the cell where I had been kept in solitary confinement. They had taken me down that long grey corridor of similar doors, a corridor which I, in my cell, had heard echo with so many footsteps, trying to deduce from their sound whether they would stop outside my door, listening for the faint clang of metal which would tell me that food was on the way. When the door of my old familiar cell had been unlocked and opened a man, having heard the footsteps halt outside his door, had risen slowly from the bunk, animal-like, to face whatever came; and I had seen in that pale prisoner myself, all prisoners, all animals in cages.

The man had looked afraid, and I had seen the same fear in the eyes of the girl in the pub in Kluse when I had gone back there. The pub where I had sat drinking with the foresters and the little policeman who had captured me was the same. It was the same girl behind the bar, but she had grown fatter and less attractive since that night in December 1942 when she had served the enemy airman with beer and sandwiches and had dried his torn and soaking clothes. She had seemed very attractive to me then, but that could have been because the wire of the prisoner-of-war camp loomed ahead. Now when I greeted her she had not seen in the clean-shaven face below the Service cap the tired, wet, frightened enemy airman she had treated with such surprising friendliness. I had asked if she remembered the airman who had been caught nearby and brought to the pub on that winter night; and it was then that I had seen the fear. Her parents had come into the room and they had all denied the airman. No airman had been brought there, they said. No airman had been shot down anywhere near there. They had never seen an English airman until now. I had felt sick at the need for their fear and denials and had explained that I had come to thank them for their kindness, not to accuse them as war criminals. Then they had remembered. They had remembered far more about that night than I had done. No, the old policeman did not get into trouble for letting me get away. Certain facts had been altered, certain times changed, and after all I had been caught in the end. Now it was all over, and would I have a drink on the house?

I drank, and learned that the policeman had gone to live with his son in another village. If I cared to walk a few miles across the fields I might find one of the foresters from whom I had escaped that night, but the man might not be home.

I had bought a round of drinks and they had left me alone standing by the bar. They spoke little English, and my German was poor. I had stood there looking round the room, noting how accurate my memory had been in some details, how widely astray in others. The room meant nothing to me now. The one I had remembered had been another room; the man who had sat there wondering how to get away, another man.

Soon the aroma of coffee began to steal down the corridor to the customs office. I heard the German word *Kaffee* repeated several times. "Make enough for four," I said. "We'll give those two a cup." She smiled, and I realised she already had. All four of us were in the small cell, drinking the coffee, when the telephone bell rang.

We had followed the jeep into the town and were sitting opposite the Colonel at a plain wooden table. There were maps on the four walls of the office and the air was thick with smoke from the Colonel's cigar. ". . . So I reckoned that while you're here you might give the men a short lecture. Some of these men weren't in the war and it will kind of give them some idea of what it was all about." He leaned back and gazed at me along the barrel of his cigar.

"I'd be glad to." I felt that even this was preferable to going right round and not getting there until after the filming had started. "Would it be possible to lay it on for this afternoon? We're in a bit of a hurry."

"Already have it laid on. Knew you wouldn't say no. Lecture in half an hour, then lunch at the Officers' Club. This afternoon I guess there's another lecture. If you don't think that's too much." It wasn't a question.

"It'll have to be the same lecture I'm afraid."

"Sure, sure. You'll be talking to the men who can't get there this morning. I've reserved accommodation for you at Haus Tannenberg tonight, over in Garmisch. It's our hotel for VIPs. I'm told it's out of this world. Just out of this world. Take up your reservations at the Billeting Office opposite the railway station. You'll be OK."

"It's very kind of you." I felt back in the RAF again, where men who sat behind desks in offices posted you from one squadron to another, or sent you at a moment's notice to some far corner of the earth to do work for which you had no aptitude. "We ought to be getting on. We've got to get up to Munsterlager to meet the film people the day after to-morrow."

"Say—just one night. You can spare one night." The Colonel expelled a cloud of blue smoke. "As a matter of fact I kinda accepted an invite for you two to take dinner with a friend of mine. Mrs Schwabe and I are going over there for dinner, and when I told him you were here, why, he insisted that we bring you over."

"We haven't any clothes," Sibyl said.

"Think nothing of it. Anything will do. But you just gotta come. Hetty just won't take 'no'."

I tried to sound firm. "It's very kind of you to take all this trouble, Colonel, but we really must leave first thing in the morning."

"Now. About your lady." The Colonel brushed the question of leaving to one side. "I have several alternative programmes for this morning. There's a shopping tour of Garmisch, or a sight-seeing tour of the surrounding country. Then this afternoon the Wives would very much appreciate a little talk."

"A talk?"

"You've had it now," I said.

"Do you mean a lecture?"

The Colonel laughed reassuringly. "No, no, just a little talk. The Wives use the Club after us. They lunch a little later than we do, and they've invited you to be the guest of honour."

She turned to me. "What shall I talk about?"

"Tell them about England," the Colonel said. "Or give them a travel talk. They love a travel talk."

I sat on the Colonel's right hand at lunch and tried to steer the conversation away from the prison camp. The trouble with accepting a meal after a lecture is that you have to go through it all again. Far better to cut and run as soon as it is over.

It had gone quite well, although I'd felt at times that it was my accent which interested them rather than my subject. I had given the lecture many times, as often as twelve times in a week, but always in the past I had lectured to aircrew and they had had a personal interest in what I had to say. I had lectured in uniform and behind locked doors, because what I had said was of value to the enemy. Now there was no enemy, and the khaki-uniformed men in front of me would not be flying out that night, or any other night, equipped with a small survival kit, a map and a pocket compass to guide them should they find themselves on foot. I remembered the zeal of my first few lectures, how I had impressed on my audience the importance of tying on their wide-topped flying boots. If you have to bale out, I'd said, the snatch of the opening parachute will jerk off your boots and you'll land without them and have to surrender. I had told them how to tie the boots so that they would not jerk off, and had once taken a motor-cycle to ride round to each aircraft at dispersal to see how many men had taken my advice. Not one member of ten crews, not one man out of seventy had taken the trouble to see that should he bale out he would have his boots on when he fell. I had mentioned this to the Intelligence Officer that night in the mess, before the crews returned, and the man had laughed. Did you fly prepared to walk home? he had asked. No, I had admitted, never thought of it. They don't think about it either, the man had said, it's never going to happen to them. Some other poor bastard, perhaps, but not to them. And thank God they do feel that way, it's their only defence poor sods.

But lecturing had soon palled. It had been interesting at first, driving from airfield to airfield, with official petrol for my car, on the empty roads of wartime England, sleeping in a different Mess each night, drinking with strange aircrew and occasionally meeting old friends from the Squadron or older friends from Training Command. Life had been simple then. You walked into the ante-room and you knew at once, from his sleeve, the rank of a man to whom you spoke. You could tell his trade from the brevet on his chest, and from the row of coloured ribbon below the brevet you could tell how he carried out that trade. Yes, it had been extraordinarily pleasant after the close confinement of the prison camp, to move around so much, so freely.

Yet soon I had tired of seeing other people off. I managed to wangle one or two trips with other crews, but it was not the same. I began to drink less and less in the Mess, to sit reading in my temporary one-night room, or to go alone to the station cinema. I missed the singleness of purpose of life in the prison camp.

It was then that I began to write the book. I wrote it bit by bit, sometimes in palatial brick-built pre-war Messes, sometimes in draughty Nissen huts; thinking about it while I drove along those empty roads, writing it down in the evening in my room, and posting what I had written to Sibyl for her to type on the Admiralty typewriter at Submarine Headquarters. She was a second officer then and far too busy to waste time on the literary outpourings of a flight lieutenant. It wasn't until later that I had learned she had sat up half the night to get it done. I had gone on writing it while I was taking the pilot's course. Some of it I'd written in Manila, and the final chapters in the *Queen Mary* coming back across the Atlantic.

That had been only the beginning, the first draft; and in the re-writing I had learned that the struggle, not only to say exactly what I meant but to find out what I did mean, gave me as great a satisfaction as shooting cleanly, or as making with my hands something that was strong and worked and was good to look at.

The conversation moved to sport and the Colonel told me how most of the deer had been eliminated in this area. "Guys go out after them in jeeps with tommy-guns," he said. "Where I come from we wouldn't go hunting with a tommy-gun. A coyote maybe, but not a deer. These city guys don't know the half of it. All they want is to kill the darn' thing. They'd do it with a bomb or poison gas if it was any easier. Say—talking of hunting, we hear you British are short of meat. Don't you have any rabbits over there?" He had been busy cutting his T-bone steak into pieces. He transferred his fork to his right hand, and began to eat.

"Oh yes," I said. "Plenty."

"Well, why don't you shoot 'em?"

"We do, Colonel. But usually they're trapped rather than shot. People find cartridges a bit expensive." I thought of the fields of Devon, lifting with rabbits. The Colonel was right of course. It was stupid when you thought of it, meat rationing while rabbits made inroads on the crops. Why didn't we kill more of them? Was food rationing the cause? Was it because people were assured of getting a subsistence amount of meat, cheaply, that they didn't bother to kill rabbits for themselves?

"Say, are you guys short of shells too? I'd be happy to let you have some shells."

"No, it's all right, really, Colonel. I'm not short."

"You say you're going to do some hunting over here?"

"I hope so."

"Well, you'll need plenty of shells. You must allow me to present you with some."

"It's very kind of you but——"

"I insist." He brushed my protestations aside. "I'll have 'em sent down to Haus Tannenberg. Y'know, you British could make a deal better proposition of your agriculture if you'd only shoot your rabbits."

"I dare say we could." I realised by now it was useless to try to swim against the tide.

"And solve your meat problem."

"Yes."

"I gather from your lecture that the Germans treated you reasonably well." The speaker was a thin studious-looking major who sat on the Colonel's other hand. "Did you get enough to eat?"

"We were always hungry for the first few weeks. But your stomach shrank after a time and you didn't notice it any more."

"There was no rough stuff?"

"Not in my experience." They always asked this. "I'm not saying there wasn't any, but I never experienced it, nor knew anyone else who did."

"Say, have you been to Dachau?" the Colonel asked.

"No."

"It's on your way. Just outside Munich. You should go there—be an eye-opener for you. It's a DP camp now. And you should stop off in Frankfurt on your way up—there's an old friend of yours there."

"Who's that?"

"Von Lindeiner."

"Oh, you've got him, have you?"

"We've got him OK."

"He was quite a decent chap, you know."

"He was Commandant of Stalag-Luft III when fifty of your men were shot."

"That wasn't his fault. The Gestapo took over. He was put in prison by them, I believe."

The Colonel laughed. "It's OK. You needn't defend him. He's being hospitalised, he's a sick man."

I thought of the stiff correct figure of the Camp Commandant walking out to take rollcall in the morning cold, his genuine dismay at the rudeness, the incorrectness of behaviour of his charges. I remembered too the feeling of security the prisoners had that they were held by the Military and not by the Gestapo. "I'd like to see him."

"I'll fix it for you," the Colonel said.

"Were there any Americans in your camp?" It was one of the officers lower down the table.

"Yes, but most of them were in a separate compound. The only ones with us were the chaps who joined the RAF before you declared war."

"Say, can you tell me why so many of your boys got away?" The Colonel leaned back in his chair and rested two large fists on the edge of the table. "I guess I don't know of a single American who escaped from a German prison camp."

I hesitated. "Perhaps there were more of us prisoners."

"No, there must be a reason," the Colonel persisted. "There were as many American Air Force prisoners as there were British—more."

"I don't really know much about it." I thought of the only American airmen I had known, those in the Eagle Squadron and others who had joined Bomber Command; men whose love of freedom or a scrap had brought them from the safety of their own country to fight in someone else's war and to spend most of it behind barbed wire. They had been good 'kriegies', as good as the best of ours.

"You must have some theory." The Colonel looked at me with his tired blue eyes. "Thirty of you Britishers got back. I want to know why none of ours did."

"There was so much luck attached to it. . . ."

"The British don't have a monopoly of luck." It seemed that he was determined to have his answer.

"Perhaps their education was at fault," I suggested.

"The American system of education is the finest in the world!"

"I don't mean academic education. I mean what you call conditioning." He was obviously waiting for me to go on. "I sat in on one of your Intelligence conferences during the war. Do you know what they discussed for two and a half hours?

What sort of candy aircrew preferred to eat while they were flying."

"I don't figure what candy's got to do with escaping." He eyed me warily.

"It just seems to me a mistake to take things like that too seriously. If you treat a man as a psychological machine he reacts by conforming to the formula."

"That just isn't an answer. What do you mean in plain words?"

Well, you asked for it, I thought. "I mean that if a man has too much attention paid to his creature comforts before he's captured, he's a bit reluctant to leave what comfort there is behind the wire."

"Huh! So you think we're soft?"

"No, it's just that once you've decided which sort of candy is best, any other sort is unheard-of. Everyone eats the same. In the end, that treatment makes men want to act in unison, and escaping is essentially a solitary business."

There was a silence.

"Of course," I said, to break the silence, "our chaps had this advantage. We've a tradition of escaping. We've a whole literature on it. Even our Prime Minister wrote an escape story. I was brought up on the escape books of the First World War."

"Haven't we any escapers in our military history?"

"There was Colonel Rose in the Civil War," the studious major said.

"That was a helluva long time ago." The Colonel glared round the table as though ordering the youngest lieutenant to go out and escape at once. "There's this to it," he added. "You've had a lot more experience in war than we have. We've only fought four foreign wars in all our history."

I worked it out. "The last two. And the one with Spain. . . ."

"And the one with you people." He looked at me suspiciously. "Don't you call that a war?"

"It's called a revolution in our history books."

"Well I'll be goddammed. . . . Is that right!"

"We sometimes call it the War of Independence."

"No, no, no! You got the wrong one," the Colonel said impatiently. "After that, in 1812, we had a war with you people."

"Oh then!" I couldn't think what to say. "I suppose we were very busy with the French about that time."

There was a noise in the ante-room like the message on a scrambler telephone amplified a hundred times. A GI rushed in looking agitated.

"Sorry Colonel, time's up."

"Say, is it as late as that?" He rose hurriedly to his feet and we slipped out by a side door, leaving our unfinished food on the table. Through the open door of the ante-room I caught sight of Sibyl, hatless, surrounded by a sea of women's hats.

When the afternoon lecture was over I went back to the Officers' Club to collect her. She was sitting in a large arm-chair thumbing through a copy of *The New Yorker*. The Wives seemed to have disappeared.

"How did it go?" I asked.

"Quite well, I think, but I'm exhausted. Have you finished now?"

"Yes, thank God. There's only the dinner, then it's all over." I looked at my watch. "It's four-thirty. Let's find this Haus Tannenberg and see if they can give us a cup of tea. We've a couple of hours before the Colonel picks us up."

In the car I said, "What did you talk to the Wives about?"

"Marriage."

"*What?*"

"Marriage."

"What did you tell them?"

"Well, actually, the Colonel's wife said they wanted to hear what it was like to become famous in England. So I told them some of the funny bits—like the old chairman, Sir Thomas Whatsisname, who fell over the table trying to read your name upside down on the front of the dais."

"You know his name very well."

"Yes. I was getting my own back. . . . And the lengths Billy went to, to duck that lecture."

I grinned as I remembered the weekend we had been invited to stay with the Publisher. I was to lecture in the village hall as a tie-up with the local bookshop, and we had arrived in the early evening to find him prostrate on a Knole settee, nursing a cold. "Ah, hello! There you are! I've been in bed all day, just got up to welcome you. Isn't it. Daren't put my face outside the door. I mean, you'll be all right by yourself this evening." All said in a voice hoarse and strained, punctuated by blowing of the nose, winces caused by a pain in the neck, whiffs at a pocket inhaler and deep medicinal draughts of whisky. The man really had looked dreadful. I had given the lecture without platform support and the next morning he had seemed much better. Before we left, his brother-in-law had called in for a drink. "Great day yesterday, Billy. Saw you take that fence at Five Mile Bottom. Best run we've had this season." The Publisher had expertly changed the subject, but the gaff had been blown.

"What else did you tell them?" I said nervously. "That wouldn't take long."

"Don't worry, I was very discreet. They asked a lot of questions. They wanted to know the finances of it. And then one of them said, wasn't it wonderful, now I'd be able to take up a career and express myself."

"What did you say?"

"I said I reckoned that in a good marriage the wife can express herself without a career of her own. That was when the trouble started—it took all the Colonel's wife's seniority to keep order."

"I must say you believe in sticking your neck out."

"Well, this morning I had a coffee in the PX cafeteria, and a great fat master-sergeant came in with his wife and three kids. The sergeant was nursing the baby, the wife ordered and paid for the meal, and the sergeant fed the children."

"How did it go down?"

"He did it very well. He seemed to be used to it."

"No, I mean your thesis."

"Oh most of them disagreed violently. My point was that the ideal was to have a full time job working with your husband, because if you work for someone else there are bound to be conflicting loyalties and one of the jobs is neglected. Most of them seem to think they're making a great sacrifice in coming out to Germany with their husbands, giving up their careers at home; so they try to run the show to compensate for it. I think the men are terrified of them."

"You should have seen how we scuttled at lunchtime."

"You were late. The Colonel's wife was furious, she sent a GI in to turn you out."

"He did too. How did it end?"

"There was one woman who said that my ideal was quite impossible nowadays. She said that when a man worked at home or in the fields he and his wife shared the running of the family unit—she called them 'partners in the project of living'. They didn't worry about sex equality, they were complementary and each did his or her own part. Even when the man went out to work for someone else, away from the home, she still had enough to occupy her. But with the invention of labour-saving devices, and the man working farther and farther away from his home so that he stayed away for lunch and only returned late at night, the woman began to get bored. The husband wasn't engaged in 'the project of living' any longer. He was out earning money in one place to support the family unit in another."

"She reckons he was having all the fun?"

"Yes. And they think it's more intelligent of the wife to go out and earn more money to pay for the labour-saving devices and for someone else to look after the children."

"In other words, there's no partnership left?"

"There doesn't seem to be. In fact I can't see why they get married, because on that basis it's only legalising the sexual relationship. And I can't see how you can better express yourself stooging in an office from nine till five with a nightmare journey each end. I suppose they really do it for companionship, or to satisfy a lust for power."

"You're a reactionary," I said. "Now if you took a steady job you could support me while I write another book. . . ."

WELCOME TO GARMISCH—EUCOM'S PLAYGROUND

The letters spanned the road in a giant archway made of wood painted red, white and blue. It was more like a film set than a real village. There were gay sunblinds, and flowers everywhere. The houses were big, with overhanging wooden roofs, and their plaster walls were decorated; some with trompe d'oeil balconies and windows, cunningly drawn cornices and mouldings, and others with allegorical and modern figures or scenes of local industry, all in soft clear colours. Each opening, door or window, had its architrave or pediment of painted arabesques, and the woodwork was beautifully carved and brightly varnished.

"It's amazing that so many marriages survive modern civilisation," I said. "Most animals leave the herd when they mate—that's the origin of the honeymoon. A marriage should be a thing outside the herd."

"That's what I tried to say. They seem to team up into couples and still go on living deep in the middle of the herd, both of them trying to do the same job. When you marry you should break away and start another herd of your own."

"Your American woman was right really. You can't do that nowadays unless you're self employed. What we need is another industrial revolution. Every man's home a workshop. Cottage industry."

"It's a much more natural existence."

"We can't go back, not unless we have a cataclysmic war and start all over again. I wonder if our civilisation *is* decadent? One of the three stages of decadence is lack of differentiation between the sexes. The sergeant's wife giving the orders and making him feed the children is only one symptom. Homosexuality is another."

"What are the other two stages?"

"Lack of differentiation between the classes, and between the species. Class first, then sex, then the species. When you grant an animal human intelligence you're well on the way down." I thought of my half cousin and her dog Alfred. She and her husband had never been abroad for a holiday in their lives, although they could well afford to. They had complained that it always rained when they took their holidays. Why not go south, I'd asked them, get down to the Mediterranean and the sun? It's all very well for you, she'd said, but we can't leave Alfie. After all, it's his holiday as much as ours.

We found Haus Tannenberg down a narrow lane in the older part of the town. A drive led to the square solid house set well back in a peaceful garden. Before the war it could have been the home of a wealthy professional man.

I stopped the car at the foot of the steps to the front door. Beneath the portico the staff were drawn up in order of seniority. I wished it hadn't rained that morning and that the car at any rate was looking spotless; I was conscious that after a fortnight out-of-doors we must be looking pretty rough.

The major-domo, in formal black, stepped forward and bowed. "I am Fritz, sir. Welcome to Haus Tannenberg." A curtsey ran down the line of servants like a wave breaking on a pebbly beach. He introduced the personal maid as Teresa and the valet as Carl, and led us through an ornate gilt-and-brocade furnished hall to our suite. The boot-boy followed with the single battered suitcase.

"Are there any other guests?" Sibyl asked.

"No madame. Haus Tannenberg is entirely at your service." Fritz bowed again and withdrew.

We inspected the formal sitting-room, the luxurious bedroom and the blue-tiled bathroom. "Pity I did the washing last night," Sibyl said, "with all this hot water laid on."

"It's a good job you did. At least some of our clothes are clean." I threw myself on the bed, which bounded up and down like an American car. "What a set-up."

"I thought they would break into song at any minute. I wonder who the VIPs usually are?"

"Journalists. People who write columns. Politicians, high church dignitaries. And film stars."

There was a soft knock on the door. It was Fritz again. "Would you care to order dinner, sir?"

"We shall be out for dinner. But we'd like some tea."

"Of course sir." He withdrew.

"I'm going to wash my hair," Sibyl said. "Then I'll have a bath. I think I'll have my tea in it."

"I dare say Fritz will bring it in to you," I said.

The Colonel's car carried us smoothly through the wooded Bavarian countryside. The windows were closed, and it was impossible to talk above the noise of dance music on the radio. The station was Eucom's own, and sometimes a tinny voice would interrupt the music to give the Command sports news, local weather reports, or announce the birthdays and weddings of members of the Occupation Forces. Then the music would start again, beating back from the windows of the car, competing with the whirr of the air-conditioner that fought a losing battle with the smoke of the Colonel's cigar. We were four people in a hermetically sealed cartridge, passing through the world but no part of it. We were isolated from the earth by hydraulic shock absorbers, protected from the buffets of the wind and the rays of the sun by tinted glass. *Oh fat white woman whom nobody loves. Why do you walk through the fields in gloves. . . .*

The dinner party was surprisingly formal and the guests did not relax until past midnight, when the hosts' two children, aged five and three, were brought downstairs in their pyjamas. There were squeals of delight from the women, throaty chuckles from the men. It seemed, as we were introduced to the thin heavy-eyed boy and sleepy girl, that this was the climax of the evening; and so it proved. As soon as the children were back in bed the guests began to take their leave.

I felt as sleepy as the children had looked, but for Colonel Schwabe the evening was just beginning. He swept us back to Garmisch and the Casa Carioca, and we drank rum and coca-cola and danced on the crowded floor. There was an ice show too, but I could not afterwards remember how the ice had got there, whether the dance floor had been rolled away to reveal the ice below or whether the floor had been flooded and then frozen. I remember that once, early in the morning, the roof had opened to reveal the night blue sky, and the stale fug of tobacco smoke had lifted to make way for the cool sweet Alpine air which swept across the noisy tables until the women had gathered their wraps about them and the roof was closed again. And I remember a vast Captain with a Scandinavian name who, in his cups, repented of his conduct in the war. With one heavy arm across my shoulder he gazed with tear-dimmed eyes into a glass of rum and coca-cola. "Jeez, I been a bastard to that little woman." He had taken a firmer grip of my shoulder with his large soft hand, "I guess I've slept with every whore from San Francisco to Singapore. Yes, sir, I been a bastard to that little woman." "You must have made a lifetime's mission of it, Ed," the Colonel had said, "there's a mighty lot of whores between San Francisco and Singapore."

At three o'clock the Colonel had a date to play poker, and he said goodbye and sent us home in his car. I was asleep almost before we started, and awoke as we turned into the drive of Haus Tannenberg. Fritz was waiting by the open door. He looked old and tired and I felt responsible, knowing that I should have told him not to wait up. On the polished floor of the entrance hall was a sealed parcel about eighteen inches square. "This is for you, sir."

"What is it?" I bent to pick it up. It was too heavy to lift.

"With Colonel Schwabe's compliments, sir."

It was the shells. I had expected a box of twenty-five—there must be twenty-five boxes here. "I can't take these."

"You must take them, sir." Fritz was firm. "The Colonel is a very rich man. It makes him feel good."

CHAPTER SEVENTEEN

THE BED was soft and the only covering was an eiderdown in a white cotton envelope. Sibyl was asleep, lying on her side, her hair across her face. I tried to do without the eiderdown but a cool wind was blowing in through the open window. I compromised by putting it across my naked stomach. Then I flung it aside, and went into the bathroom for a drink of water. Can't take it now, I thought. There had been a time, when I was flying, when I had dealt with a lot more alcohol than this—but had sweated most of it out on the squash court, or in fear in my flying jacket. I downed three glasses of water and went back into the bedroom.

Sibyl was sitting, her hands clasped round her drawn-up legs. "I've been thinking," she said.

"Oh no! Not now!" I climbed back into bed and pulled the eiderdown up round my neck, leaving my feet uncovered. "Well, what about?"

"It's the last day of our holiday. We don't want to spend all morning lying in bed nursing a hangover."

"It's not half past four yet. Breakfast isn't until nine, so you might as well go back to sleep."

"That's the point. We don't want to hang about waiting for breakfast. We've a long way to go before tomorrow evening, and we ought to have a look at Dachau. And there's the hospital in Frankfurt."

"If you think I'm sliding out of this place as if I've stolen the silver . . ."

"Oh darling. We can leave a note for Fritz. We've said goodbye to the Colonel. And we've lashings of eggs and bacon, we might just as well eat out-of-doors while we can."

"You're greedy," I told her. "You always think it's the last time and try to make the most of it."

"I know." She looked serious for a moment.

"All right." I got out of bed. "I'll shower while you have your bath. And you'd better hurry. It would be awful to be caught in the act."

Within twenty minutes we had dressed, packed the suitcase and written the note for Fritz. We tiptoed out to the entrance hall, and I was fervently grateful that the suite was on the ground floor. It would have been too farcical to have had to negotiate creaking stairs. With some difficulty we lifted the parcel of cartridges. Sibyl unbolted, unlocked and opened the heavy door, and I staggered out. "Before we close this for ever behind us," I said, "You'd better just nip back and see that we haven't forgotten anything. I'll stow the luggage."

"I'm sure we haven't."

A few minutes later she ran down the steps and climbed into the car. I coasted silently down the sloping drive and turned into the lane. We came to a standstill where some thick shrubs hid us from the windows of the house and I switched on the engine. We waited while she warmed up. "Well, what was it you'd forgotten?"

"The roe."

"What on earth did you unpack it for?"

"I put it on the table between the beds."

"You're sentimental, that's your trouble." I let in the clutch and we moved off through the quiet clean streets towards the open country. On the outskirts of the town we passed under another wooden archway. "And so we say goodbye to Eucom's Playground, Eucom's Winter Wonderland. . . ."

"It's the wrong time of day," she said. "There's always a setting sun sinking into the sea behind the island when they say that. This is the beginning of the film."

We were leaving the high mountains behind, driving along a flat straight road through a broad green valley. The morning was cold and a white mist hung low over the meadows. Moving fast now in the open car I felt the air fresh on my face, blowing away the stale cigarette-laden atmosphere of the Casa Carioca. It's not worth it, I thought. This is what matters. Willi was right.

"Isn't this exciting," Sibyl said; and I grinned and knew that she had guessed my thought.

"You were born in a field with the gate open," I said. "I'll get excited when I can smell that bacon frying. Let's stop on the edge of this wood."

A chill wind was clearing the mist and I put up the tent so that she could cook in its lee. I struggled with the guy ropes on the windward side. "The things I do for you. . . . Any sensible man would be lying in bed at this hour, recuperating."

"Think how much better you'll feel."

"I couldn't feel any worse. Every time I hammer a tent peg some chap comes up behind me and clocks me over the head. What I want is a strong cup of coffee, and no nonsense."

"We've got visitors," she said quickly. "And don't you dare offer *them* coffee. We're keeping the last two tins for von Lindeiner."

I peered round the tent and saw a party of two men and two women picking their way carefully, in Indian file, across the field. All four carried small aluminium milk churns and they had a look of exaggerated nonchalance as though they were approaching a herd of deer when there is no cover. The leader was a short plump man with a goatee beard, wearing plus-fours and a narrow-brimmed Tyrolean hat with the tail feather of a blackcock stuck jauntily in the band. He carried a furled umbrella which he used as an Alpenstock. The tall lean man behind him wore a cloak of green loden like the boy in the deer forest had worn, and one of the two women who brought up the rear was dressed in Bavarian peasant costume, with a full red dirndl skirt. "One thing I like about the Germans," I said, "is the way they dress up for everything. Look at these. They're obviously city people, but they're on holiday so they dress the part. No German would think of motoring without a leather coat and helmet—and no German would dream of going on holiday in Bavaria without the walking stick covered with badges, a Tyrolean hat and *lederhosen*. The woman in the raincoat must be a foreigner." I hammered in the last tent peg, as the Germans arrived.

"*Guten Morgen*," I heard Sibyl say.

"Good morning." The short plump leader stood at attention, coughed to clear his throat and recited:

> "Twinkle, twinkle, little star,
> How I wonder what you are . . ."

He paused, and feeling that some comment was expected I said, "Bravo!" But I was wrong. He continued:

> "Up above the world so high,
> Like a candle in the sky."

I waited a moment, to make sure that this was the end, and then all I could think of was, "Diamond. Not candle."

"*Ach* yes. Diamond. It is thirty-five years since I have said that." He beamed at us proudly through rimless pince-nez.

"You remember it very well," Sibyl told him. She lowered the flame under the frying-pan.

The professor, I could not help thinking of him as a professor, moved round behind the car. "*GB. Grosbritannien.* You are the first English I have spoken to since before the war. You have come from the British Zone?"

"No, we're on holiday." It seemed the simplest explanation.

"*Ach so!* Germany is free now to accept holiday-makers?" The tall man sounded bitter.

"You wouldn't have thought so at the border," I told him. "They didn't seem too keen to let us in."

"You like Germany?" the professor asked.

"Yes. Very much."

"Poor Germany," the woman in the red dirndl said. "How we have suffered."

"We have a house," the professor said. "It is only a small house we built before the war, to visit from Munich at the weekends. But it is a roof over our heads. That is more than can be said for many. It is on the other side of the wood. If you will visit us, we shall be honoured."

"It's very kind of you," I said, "but we're about to have breakfast. Will you join us in a drink?" The only thing we had to offer was whisky, and I took the flask and the leather case of tumblers from the pocket of the car and poured the thin amber spirit. "There's no soda I'm afraid. Will you have water with it?"

"Is it English whisky?"

"No. Scotch. Do you like whisky?"

"I have never tasted it. Do not put the water in it please." He stuck his umbrella upright in the ground, removed his hat and perched it on the handle. This was to be a ceremony of some importance. The tall thin man accepted a tumbler, silently bowing his thanks, but the women refused. From the professor's sharp look in their direction I realised that it would have been an impertinence for them to accept. Whisky was a masculine drink.

"*Prosit!*" Everyone had toasted, heels were clicked. A

tentative sip, then down with the lot. The professor gasped in admiration. The tall thin man took a tin from his pocket and hastily swallowed a white tablet. The professor beamed. "It is an English custom to drink whisky before breakfast?"

"Always," I said solemnly. Even though in my case it was the hair of the dog it was worth it, to show the flag.

The professor replaced his hat. "It is good, the fellowship of the open air, to sleep under the stars. It is romantic."

"It is cold, *nicht*?" The woman in the raincoat was German after all.

"Not really," Sibyl said. "We have these." She showed the women the eiderdown sleeping bags while I persuaded the professor to have another whisky. The tall man decided not to risk it again.

"Germany is a good country for wandering," the professor said. "When I am young I have done much. Will you not light the camp fire?"

"I don't think so," I said. "We shall be moving on straight after breakfast."

"*Ach*, it is a pity you have not the fire. To sit round the camp fire and sing songs, it is so *lustig*."

"Neither of us can sing a note. Will you have another whisky?"

"No thank you. You have already been so kind. We will leave you to your camping." He gathered his party together. "It is a pity you have not the camp fire. . . . Where do you go from here?"

"To Dachau." I said it without thinking, and to judge by their expression I might have said something obscene. The tall man bowed frigidly and turned and hustled the women away. The professor held his ground alone.

"Do not judge Germany by Dachau," he said. "The German people were ignorant of what was taking place."

I was sorry to have upset the old man, but I had heard this so often before. "Not all of them surely?"

He stood there looking at me, a mild romantic kindly little man. "We, the German people, were ignorant," he said. "It has needed two world wars to teach us that a nation of free men is stronger than a common cause. *Auf wiedersehen*." He retrieved his umbrella, and hurried after his companions.

The concentration camp at Dachau was still occupied by

the former prisoners of Germany, but now as Displaced Persons. Only the crematorium and the gas chamber were open to public view and these had been cleaned up and set out as a museum. There was a guide on duty, a German, who explained how the poison gas had been introduced into the communal shower-bath and pointed out the incinerators where the bodies had been burned and the hooks from which the prisoners had been hanged. All this he did without emotion, neither approving nor disapproving, speaking in the impersonal manner of a professional guide and as though all that had happened here had happened many years ago. I wondered whether he had been a prisoner, a guard, or one of those Germans who were ignorant of what was taking place. They have put it all in the past, I thought, and consider themselves as guiltless of this as we are of the torture of the Bloody Tower, or the French of the Reign of Terror. I turned my back on Dachau with a feeling of relief and wondered why we had come out of our way to see the place. It wasn't exactly rubbernecking. I'd always been treated reasonably well as a prisoner and found it difficult to believe that man could do the things I had read about at the end of the war. There seemed to be no doubt.

We drove back towards Munich to join the Autobahn on the outskirts of the city, and the long drive north through Germany began. The road did not cut mechanically straight across the countryside but wound gently along its contours, so that although it was man-made it fitted unobtrusively into the landscape. Driving along it was almost like ski-ing in a succession of long and graceful curves through the rolling hills and dark forests which were dominated by a sky of high black fast-moving clouds. There were no crossroads. The minor roads either passed over bridges or through tunnels, and joined the correct side of the Autobahn by tributary lanes which ran in at an acute angle, never obstructing the main road traffic, and reducing the risk of collision to a minimum.

There were no advertising hoardings like those which had made the Italian Autostrada hideous, no stink of exhaust fumes in spite of the black-tailed diesel lorries, no feeling of running on a railway track. There were few German traffic signs, but the Americans had erected huge hoardings; some reassuring the motorist with the distance in miles to the next Comfort Station, others reminding him that DEATH IS SO PER-

MANENT with crude drawings of skulls and crossbones, and figures recording how many deaths the road had caused that year. Occasionally there was a battered or burned-out car or jeep left on the verge, the grim warning underlined by a large notice explaining why the wreck was there.

Now, again, no pedestrian, cyclist or horse-drawn traffic was allowed on the two broad lanes of the Autobahn and the lorries, vans and cars streamed steadily and swiftly in opposite directions. The Bentley was running sweetly and smoothly, and I felt a surge of joy each time we passed a big new American saloon. Sibyl was silent, obviously perfectly happy.

"A road like this could only be made in a totalitarian state," I said. "Imagine trying to do it in England. It's not only the cost of building it. It's all the front gardens, rights of way, ancient monuments you'd have to sweep out of its path. I must say this is rather pleasant though."

And it's only in a totalitarian state, I thought, that Dachau could exist, with the bulk of the population ignorant of what was taking place. Were they? When you sink your own identity in a cause you surrender the right to question. *Befehl ist Befehl.* Orders are orders. My country right or wrong. The Roman soldier standing at his post as the ashes mounted round him. How admirable in one way, how dangerous in another.

There was Madge, mother of six children, Madge who would give you her last shilling and share with you her last crust of bread. But Madge the Communist who would cheerfully see men, women and children stood up against a wall and shot if such an act, which she acknowledged as horrible in itself, would lead to world Communism. At first I had not believed her, but in the end I had been convinced that she meant what she said. In that plump good-natured middle-aged woman dwelled a fanatic. With Madge, Communism was a religion, and would not Abraham have given up his son?

The professor had been right. *A nation of free men is stronger than a common cause.* No matter how common the cause, no matter what material results are acheived by unity, its followers collapse at its defeat. A nation of free men will fight for ever, one individual springing up as another is mown down.

We stopped in a lay-by beside a stretch of short grass under trees, set out with stone tables and seats and wastepaper baskets, overlooking a wooded valley now glowing with the greens and browns of full summer. In the silence that followed the stopping of the engine we heard steps behind us and, turning, saw a queer unkempt figure emerge from the cover of the trees and come hesitatingly across the grass. He was dressed in threadbare remnants of German army uniform and on his skull-like head he wore a battered military ski-cap. His luggage, such as it was, he carried in a sack worn like a haversack under one arm, and his feet were bound in rags.

"*Guten Tag*," I said.

He did not seem to be aware of us at all but stared unblinkingly at the stone table, now crowded with the jar of butter and the dish of tomatoes, the large brown German loaf and the long sausage that Sibyl had bought in Munich early that morning. I poured a whisky and offered it to him but he shook his head. Sibyl spread a thick slice of bread with butter and cut a chunk off the hard sausage, and he moved nearer and held out a shaking hand. Then he shuffled a few steps away and, slumping on to the bench at the next table, tore at the food like an animal. I've been hungry in my time, but never so hungry as that. I put the whisky down on the table beside him and left him to eat alone.

We began our meal in silence. After a few minutes the man shambled over and put down the empty tumbler, mumbling thanks. I indicated the bench at our table, and he sat down.

Conversation was difficult, both because of our poor German and because the man seemed to be out of the habit of speaking. He seemed content to sit there, with more bread and sausage, eating it slowly this time; but we learned that he had been released from a labour camp in Siberia a month ago and was walking home from the border where the Russians had set him loose. He had heard nothing of his wife and family since his capture in 1942, but was making for Stuttgart where they had lived before the war. He did not seem anxious to get there, to find out what had happened to them in the last seven years, what his own life was to be from now on. He seemed dazed, as though to be free was enough for the moment, to be free to walk along the edge of the Autobahn through the summer countryside, and to meet calamity, if it was to be calamity, in his own full time. I tried to learn from him what life had been like in a Russian prison camp, how it felt to be held prisoner so long after the war was finished, but he was non-committal in his replies. It seemed that for him the past was finished, that he had no faith in the future, that the present was merely the momentary satisfaction of an animal need, to be accepted without curiosity or question.

We left him still sitting on the bench, leaning heavily on his elbows on the table; and as I settled down to the steady rhythm of driving along the wide open road that left so much time for thinking, I wondered what would happen to the man. His wife might be dead, or moved to another town, or living with someone else, or working for the Occupying Power in another Zone—or any of the other thousand more likely things than being where he had left her. But even if she were none of these things and he found her without difficulty, how could he pick up the thread of the life he had left over seven years before? A lot can happen to a man, or a woman, in seven years. No wonder he had been reluctant to talk about the future, almost as though he were frightened to end his present journey.

Von Lindeiner had a private ward, but the man who rose as I entered was not the immaculate officer I remembered. Six years ago he had been wearing Luftwaffe uniform and jack-boots, and braided silver thread of an *Oberst* on the shoulder-straps and the Iron Cross on the breast pocket of his tunic. Now he wore bedroom slippers and a woollen dressing-gown. He had shrunk, and looked as though he had little longer to live and nothing to look forward to.

"I don't know whether you remember me, sir. Flight Lieutenant Williams."

He smiled. "Ah yes. They told me you were coming. The wooden horse man."

I put the small parcel on the table by the high hospital bed. "I thought you might like some English coffee." But I knew as I said it that my remark was tactless. After the mass escape the Commandant had been accused of black market transactions in food from British Red Cross parcels. I talked fast, anxious to give the impression that such a cowardly hint had not been my intention, knowing that it had been a mistake to come. I was so much this man's junior in age and rank that any approach seemed impertinent or patronising, and I wished I had not been so enthusiastic when Colonel Schwabe had suggested the visit.

We talked about the camp, and Von Lindeiner seemed interested to know what had happened to the Senior British Officer, and to Mike and Oliver, but our successful tunnel had been the beginning of the end for the Camp Commandant and I did not feel that the memories I evoked were pleasant. I did not stay for long and was glad to escape from the confinement of the small room down the echoing corridors and out through the swing doors into the freedom of the open air.

Sibyl was waiting in the car. "You were very quick," she said.

"There was really nothing to say."

"You wish you hadn't gone."

"It seemed like kicking a man when he's down. One should never try to go back, it's always a mistake."

We had driven hard for the rest of the evening but darkness caught us still on the Autobahn, with two hundred and fifty miles to cover the next day. I pulled off into the fringe of the pine forest which stretched for miles on either side of the road. A storm threatened, but there was a high wind and the dark clouds were strained across the sky. Tired by the day's long journey I erected the tent in silence, and Sibyl set up the stove and cooked the evening meal by the light of the headlamps.

I wished now that we had driven farther into the forest, away from the Autobahn. There was something in the presence of the road that made me uneasy. Camping in the mountains, away from busy highways, had seemed a natural thing. Here on the edge of civilisation yet away from habitation, it was another matter. Not long ago the Autobahn had been a route for displaced persons, liberated Russian prisoners of war, and Nazi thugs in disguise travelling with the mob, raping and pillaging as they went. By now most of them had been rounded up, but I had noticed one or two ugly customers on the fringe of the road as we had passed. The man at lunchtime for instance. He had been alone, but supposing a gang of them were to come along? This place was too near the road, too near the artery along which the riffraff of the towns would flow.

That night I lay on my bed with the axe beside my knee. Tired as I was I could not sleep. I started at every sound. Every thud of a falling pine cone brought me to a state of tension, lying with held breath to catch the sound of footsteps. I thought of the theft in the night on the shore of the lake, the hand stealing under the canvas of the tent so near our heads. Supposing a gang of them were to come now? I hadn't much money with me. But there was Sibyl. I had the axe, but how far could you go in defending your integrity? Supposing the men came now, intruding on the privacy of this tent? Which was the moment when you could use the axe, certain that it was in defence and not aggression? It was a matter for you alone to decide. It would be futile to rely on the police, on law and order. There were no police here, now, and the fact that the violaters would not go unpunished would be no recompense.

I tried to dismiss the fears as nonsense, but they would not go. It was useless to say that such things did not happen nowadays. Here in Germany not long ago there had been mass killings and torture unprecedented. In a flash the German people had been turned from one of the most law-abiding nations into one in which human life and dignity had been set at nothing. The only dignity was the integrity of self-reliance. The bigger the herd, the more part of the herd a man became, the less chance he had of retaining this integrity. Man's instinct is to struggle for a living. He is really only happy, in youth, in struggle. Peace and security are for old age.

And what about the security of my job? It was no use us putting off the decision. If I were leaving Lewis's I should tell them soon, not wait until the six months were up. I wanted it both ways. Freedom with security. The two seldom went together. Ever since I had first wondered what I should do on leaving school I had envisaged some sort of employment with a large concern. Most of the boys at school with me had thought the same. A Bank, an Insurance Company, an Oil Company, or Government Service. You had to pass an exam to get in and if you got in you could still play games, and you worked with a crowd of decent chaps. It was a prolongation of school and waived the necessity of growing up. And Lewis's had been so much a part of my life for so many years. There was security inside that walled city, presided over by its board of wise men, governed by its hierarchy of managers and assistant managers each in his own well-defined niche with its attendant privileges. It wasn't only the salary and the pension at the end of it, it was the feeling of belonging to an ordered scheme of things. You were privileged, cushioned against the necessity of coping with so many details. The firm would arrange a mortgage on your house, or move you lock, stock and barrel from one of their branches to another. Manufacturers would produce exactly the article you required; there were no shortages for a firm that bought in such large quantities. For everything you bought you paid less than the retail price. *Take what you will.* . . . You paid in full, of course, but in another way. The price was freedom, and I had learned to value freedom.

Lying sleepless in that small tent I grinned at myself as I thought of the many self-employed free men who would be amazed at my hesitation, but those who had always been independent would never realise how difficult the break could be. . . .

I must have dozed. Then I was awake, tense on my bed, waiting. An engine had just been switched off on the road below and I could hear soft guttural German voices. It was impossible to tell whether it was a car or a lorry. In the moment of waking I knew that an engine had stopped, and that was all. I pulled on my trousers and crouched with the unlit torch in one hand and in the other the axe, waiting. Then I groped for my shoes. I'd meet them outside the tent where there was room to move around.

The dark bulking figure of a man was stepping cautiously across the strip of wet grass between the road and the trees. Behind him were lights and the silhouette of a saloon car. I straightened myself and started to walk towards him, the axe swinging from my hand. "*Was wollen Sie?*"

The man stopped. He was not so big as he had seemed at first. I flashed my torch and saw spectacles and a town overcoat of dark cloth and soft felt hat. He held out his hands and began to speak.

"*Ich bin Englander,*" I said. "*Nicht verstehen!*"

"Forgive me." The German spoke now in halting English. "My engine boils. Have you water, please?"

Back in the tent, I realised that in the moment of walking out to meet the man I had been completely happy. Always, all my life, I had been frightened before the event but at the time, when I had accepted in its simplicity the fact that I must fight, the fear had gone.

I knew that Sibyl was right. Only by leaving Lewis's, by standing on my own two feet, would I find something worth the telling. I would not wake her now, it would keep until the morning.

Before I fell asleep again I heard the rain come, slow heavy drops, like small pebbles thrown against the canvas of the tent.

THESE ARE PAN BOOKS—

Olle Strandberg

JAMBO!

A fantastic two-year adventure—60,000 miles in a Land Rover around Africa. Exciting incidents on every page. It contains poignant and exciting photographs of the bizarre juxtaposition of old and new Africa. (2/6)

Jens Bjerre

THE LAST CANNIBALS

The author of this exciting book lived among ferocious cannibals who still inhabit remote parts of New Guinea, witnessing their magic rituals and secret ceremonies. He also visited the naked 'Stone Age' Aborigines of Central Australia, ate caterpillars and lizards, attended the grim tribunal initiation of boys and the extraordinary ceremony of the Great Snake. *Illustrated* (2/6)

Sir Mortimer Wheeler

STILL DIGGING

Television's 'Personality of the Year', who introduced millions to the thrills of archæology, tells with humour and gusto the story of his exciting career. *Illustrated* (2/6)

A. F. Tschiffely

TSCHIFFELY'S RIDE

Ride from the Argentine to the United States? Impossible! the experts told the young schoolmaster who had conceived this idea. But, undaunted, he set out from Buenos Aires with his two faithful horses, Mancha and Gato. Braving extremes of heat and cold, facing danger from sudden accidents, wild animals, poisonous insects. Tschiffely emerged from his ordeal truimphant, reaching Washington after the longest journey ever attempted by man and horse. *Illustrated* (2/6)

PICK OF THE PAPERBACKS

Graham Greene

JOURNEY WITHOUT MAPS

The record of Graham Greene's travels on foot through 350 miles of roadless and disease-infested forest in the Negro Republic of Liberia. Mr Greene links his observations of Liberia with frank comments and parallels with European ways of life making his book disturbing and provocative. *Illustrated* (2/6)

Heinrich Harrer

SEVEN YEARS IN TIBET

Heinrich Harrer, a well-known Austrian mountaineer and ski-ing champion, was interned by the British in India at the outbreak of war. He escaped into Tibet and, after extraordinary adventures, reached the Forbidden City of Lhasa, where he began a strange new life and became the first European ever to be allowed close contact with the young Dali Lama, the god-king. *Illustrated* (2/6)

Sir Michael Bruce

TRAMP ROYAL

The man who can't escape adventure tells his life-story. 'A frenziedly adventurous life. The book is so easy and exciting to read that it is only after it has been shut that one realises how much the kind of man it describes has faded out of contemporary writing.'—*Punch. Illustrated* (2/6)

Ronnie Noble

SHOOT FIRST

Grit, cheek, luck—the author needed all these in filming some of the most exciting events of our time for the news-reels of cinema and television. His book is packed with racy stories of his experiences. *Illustrated* (2/6)